Y0-BXQ-631

TRANSITION METAL ORGANOMETALLICS IN ORGANIC SYNTHESIS

Volume II

This is Volume 33 of
ORGANIC CHEMISTRY
A series of monographs
Editor: HARRY H. WASSERMAN

A complete list of the books in this series appears at the end of the volume.

TRANSITION METAL ORGANOMETALLICS IN ORGANIC SYNTHESIS

Volume II

EDITED BY

Howard Alper
Department of Chemistry
University of Ottawa
Ottawa, Ontario, Canada

QD262
T7
V. 2
1978

ACADEMIC PRESS   New York   San Francisco   London   1978

A Subsidiary of Harcourt Brace Jovanovich, Publishers

343267

COPYRIGHT © 1978, BY ACADEMIC PRESS, INC.
ALL RIGHTS RESERVED.
NO PART OF THIS PUBLICATION MAY BE REPRODUCED OR
TRANSMITTED IN ANY FORM OR BY ANY MEANS, ELECTRONIC
OR MECHANICAL, INCLUDING PHOTOCOPY, RECORDING, OR ANY
INFORMATION STORAGE AND RETRIEVAL SYSTEM, WITHOUT
PERMISSION IN WRITING FROM THE PUBLISHER.

ACADEMIC PRESS, INC.
111 Fifth Avenue, New York, New York 10003

United Kingdom Edition published by
ACADEMIC PRESS, INC. (LONDON) LTD.
24/28 Oval Road, London NW1   7DX

Library of Congress Cataloging in Publication Data

Main entry under title:

Transition metal organometallics in organic
    synthesis.

    (Organic chemistry series)
    Includes bibliographies and indexes.
    1. Chemistry, Organic--Synthesis. 2. Organo-
metallic compounds. 3. Transition metal compounds.
I. Alper, Howard. II. Series.
QD262.T7   547'.2   75-40604
ISBN 0-12-053102-X (v. 2)

PRINTED IN THE UNITED STATES OF AMERICA

CONTENTS

1 THE POTENTIAL UTILITY OF TRANSITION METAL–ALKYNE COMPLEXES AND DERIVED CLUSTER COMPOUNDS AS REAGENTS IN ORGANIC SYNTHESIS
Kenneth M. Nicholas, Mara O. Nestle, and Dietmar Seyferth

2 ARENE COMPLEXES IN ORGANIC SYNTHESIS
Gérard Jaouen

v

3 OXIDATION, REDUCTION, REARRANGEMENT, AND OTHER SYNTHETICALLY USEFUL PROCESSES

Howard Alper

LIST OF CONTRIBUTORS

Numbers in parentheses indicate the pages on which the authors' contributions begin.

Howard Alper (121), Department of Chemistry, University of Ottawa, Ottawa, Ontario, Canada K1N 6N5

Gérard Jaouen (65), Laboratoire de Chimie des Organométalliques, Université de Rennes, 35031 Rennes Cedex, France

Mara O. Nestle (1), Department of Chemistry, Massachusetts Institute of Technology, Cambridge, Massachusetts 02139

Kenneth M. Nicholas (1), Department of Chemistry, Boston College, Chestnut Hill, Massachusetts 02167

Dietmar Seyferth (1), Department of Chemistry, Massachusetts Institute of Technology, Cambridge, Massachusetts 02139

PREFACE TO VOLUME I

Transition metal organometallic chemistry has been one of the most active areas of chemical research for the past twenty-five years. A significant part of this research has been concerned with the use of transition metal organometallics in organic synthesis. This two-volume work reviews the literature in this area with particular emphasis on the most effective synthetic transformations.

In Volume I, the versatility of olefin complexes in organic synthesis is amply demonstrated in Chapter 1 by Birch and Jenkins. Noyori has summarized the extensive work on coupling reactions of σ-bonded and π-allyl complexes. In the final chapter of Volume I, Casey considers both achievements and possible areas of use of metal–carbene complexes.

In Volume II, which will be published in the near future, the following topics will be covered: The Potential Utility of Transition Metal–Alkyne Complexes and Derived Cluster Compounds as Reagents in Organic Synthesis (K. M. Nicholas, M. O. Nestle, and D. Seyferth); Arene Complexes in Organic Synthesis (G. Jaouen); and Oxidation, Reduction, Rearrangement, and Other Synthetically Useful Processes (H. Alper).

An important consideration in discussing stoichiometric reactions is the ease of complexation and decomplexation of the ligands in question. The catalytic area is examined in less detail than the stoichiometric area since reviews of catalytic applications of transition metal organometallics exist in the literature.

This book will be a useful reference for synthetic organic and organometallic chemists and for inorganic chemists who wish to become acquainted with the applications of these organometallic complexes as reagents and catalysts. It should also prove useful to graduate students, either as a reference or as a text for a specialized course in synthesis.

I am grateful to the contributors of this volume and to the staff of Academic Press for their splendid cooperation.

Howard Alper

PREFACE TO VOLUME II

As noted in the Preface to Volume I, the second volume includes chapters on the applications of arene and alkyne complexes, as well as cluster compounds, in organic synthesis. Other useful synthetic transformations are discussed in the last chapter. A chapter on insertion reactions of synthetic utility was not included, due to the publication in the last few years of a substantial number of fine reviews in this area.

Howard Alper

1

THE POTENTIAL UTILITY OF TRANSITION METAL–ALKYNE COMPLEXES AND DERIVED CLUSTER COMPOUNDS AS REAGENTS IN ORGANIC SYNTHESIS

KENNETH M. NICHOLAS, MARA O. NESTLE,
and DIETMAR SEYFERTH

1

Copyright © 1978 by Academic Press, Inc.
All rights of reproduction in any form reserved.
ISBN 0–12–053102–X

I. INTRODUCTION

Transition metal compounds of diverse types undergo reactions with alkynes to yield a large variety of organometallic and organic products. In some cases, simple acetylene complexes are obtained. Often, however, more complex ligands result from insertion or oligomerization reactions. Undoubtedly, the formation of the latter products in most cases proceeds by way of initially formed acetylene complexes, but these are often undetectable.

It is our intent in this chapter to point out the potential utility of transition metal–alkyne complexes and cluster compounds which may be derived from them as reagents in organic synthesis. In the interests of brevity, we have chosen to limit the discussion to the organic chemistry of isolable acetylene complexes. Those reactions of particular synthetic promise for which alkyne complexes have not been demonstrated to be intermediates, but whose course very likely involves such complexes, will be mentioned only briefly.

We shall begin with a brief discussion of the bonding and structures of alkyne complexes and a survey of their preparation. In discussing the chemistry of these complexes, it is convenient to subdivide their reactions into two categories: (1) those in which the coordinated triple bond is unaffected, and (2) those in which the coordinated triple bond is the reactive center. These reactions may yield organic products directly or may first produce organometallic species which may potentially be transformed in a subsequent step into organic products. This latter step often has been neglected by organometallic chemists, thus limiting somewhat the synthetic utilization of such reactions. Our main purpose, therefore, is not only to highlight those reactions of proved synthetic value but also to point out fertile ground for future cultivation. Useful reviews are available (Hubel, 1968; Bowden and Lever, 1968; Otsuka and Nakamura, 1976a; Dickson and Fraser, 1974; Hartley, 1969) which provide more complete discussions of the preparation, bonding and structure, and reactivity of particular classes of alkyne complexes.

II. BONDING AND STRUCTURE OF METAL–ALKYNE COMPLEXES

Metal–alkyne bonding generally is considered to be dominated by two orbital interactions (Figs. 1a and 1b) which act synergistically (Dewar, 1951; Chatt and Duncanson, 1953; Maitlis, 1971a,c; Nelson and Jonassen, 1971).

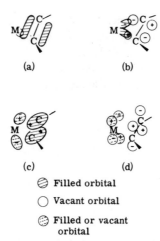

(a) (b)

(c) (d)

⊘ Filled orbital

◯ Vacant orbital

⊗ Filled or vacant
orbital

Fig. 1 Bonding interactions for the coordinated alkyne (Otsuka and Nakamura, 1976a). (a) $\pi_{\parallel}$ (alkyne) → dsp (metal), (b) dp (metal) → $\pi_{\parallel}^*$ (alkyne), (c) $\pi_{\perp}$ (alkyne) → ρ (metal), (d) d (metal) → $\pi_{\perp}^*$ (alkyne).

Contributions involving ligand and metal orbitals which are perpendicular to the metal–alkyne plane, e.g., Figs. 1c and 1d, are likely to be less important due to less efficient orbital overlap. The relative contributions of the structures in Figs. 1a and 1b are, of course, dependent upon the effective oxidation state of the metal, the nature of auxiliary ligands present, and the substituents on the alkyne. Thus, the σ-bonding component (see Fig. 1a), which involves ligand-to-metal charge transfer, is dominant for the earlier transition metals or those in higher oxidation states. Backbonding from metal to ligand (Fig. 1b) becomes increasingly important for the later transition elements, for those in low effective oxidation states, and for alkynes bearing electron-withdrawing substituents. In valence bond terms, the bonding in alkyne complexes may be represented as shown below:

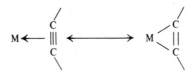

Either picture qualitatively rationalizes two important structural features of the coordinated alkyne: (1) the C≡C bond order is decreased relative to that in the free ligand, and (2) its geometry is cis, bent. Analogy has been drawn between the structures of the coordinated alkyne and the excited state of the free ligand (Blizzard and Santry, 1968). Carbon–carbon bond lengths in coordinated alkynes range from 1.24 to 1.40 Å, and the deformation angle (deviation from linearity) typically is 20°–50° (Otsuka and Nakamura, 1976b). The structures of a few complexes which illustrate these effects are shown below (Glanville et al., 1967; Davies et al., 1970; Sly, 1959). As can be seen in the first two examples, an increase in the metal's effective oxidation state decreases back-bonding and leads to lesser lengthening of the C≡C bond.

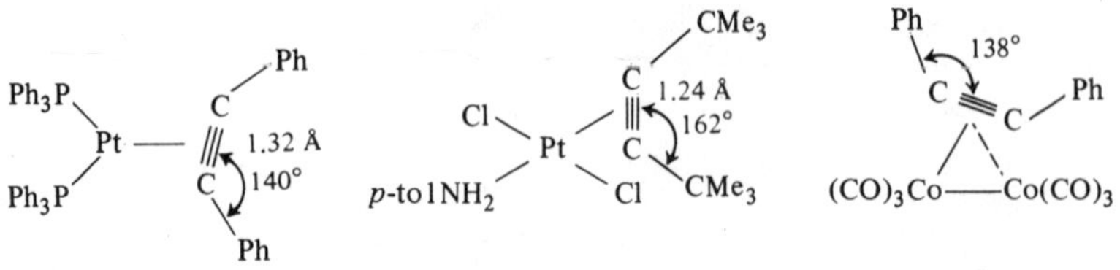

The effects of coordination also are manifested in the infrared spectra of metal–alkyne complexes. The C≡C stretching vibration of coordinated alkynes typically is in the 1700–2000 cm^{-1} region (Otsuka and Nakamura, 1976b). The decrease in stretching frequency of the triple bond upon coordination also correlates roughly with the extent of metal–ligand π-bonding. Thus Pt(II)Cl$_2$(RC≡CR)L or [Pt(II)CH$_3$(RC≡CR)L$_2$]$^+$PF$_6^-$ (Mann et al., 1971) exhibits a band at about 2000 cm^{-1} (ca. 250 cm^{-1} lower than for the free acetylene), whereas Pt(O)(RC≡CR)L$_2$ (Davidson, 1972) shows a band in the range 1680–1850 cm^{-1}.

The increased olefinic character of the coordinated alkyne is reflected in several aspects of the ^{1}H and ^{13}C nmr spectra of alkyne complexes. The nmr resonances of coordinated acetylenic hydrogens frequently appear in the olefinic region, e.g., at δ6.0–6.5 for the common L$_2$Pt(RC≡CH) (Nelson and Jonassen, 1971) and (RC≡CH)Co$_2$(CO)$_6$ (Iwashita et al., 1971) complexes. Evidence for increased p-character of the acetylenic carbons upon complexation is provided from values of ^{13}C—H coupling constants. For example, $^1J(^{13}$C—H$) = 210$ Hz for (Ph$_3$P)$_2$Pt(HC≡CH) (Cook and Wan, 1970). Carbon-13 nmr, which potentially could provide valuable bonding and structural information, has not yet been used widely in the study of metal–alkyne complexes. Whereas the coordinated acetylenic carbons in (Ph$_3$P)$_2$-Pt(CH$_3$C≡CCH$_3$) resonate at δ112.8 ppm (Chisholm et al., 1972) (ca. 40 ppm downfield from that of the free ligand), the coordination shifts ($\Delta\delta$ ^{13}C) of (RC≡CR')Co$_2$(CO)$_6$ are smaller ($+5$ to -20 ppm) (Todd and Wilkinson, 1974; Aimé et al., 1977), but still generally downfield. These data are consistent with the increased olefinic character of the coordinated alkyne. Although attempts have been made to interpret the magnitude of the coordination shifts (Aimé et al., 1977), it appears that quantitative correlation of $\Delta\delta$ ^{13}C with *individual* bonding or structural parameters (e.g., π-electron density, hybridization, the balance between σ- and π-metal–ligand bonding) is not possible.

III. PREPARATION OF METAL–ALKYNE COMPLEXES

A. General Methods of Preparation

Alkyne complexes of virtually every transition metal are known. The range of structural types is striking—included are compounds with one, two, or three acetylenes, a similar range in the number of metal atoms, and a variety of ancillary ligands such as carbon monoxide, phosphines, halides, cyclopentadienyl, and others.

Preparative information for selected complexes is presented in Table 1. The listing is not exhaustive but is limited instead to those classes of compounds for which a few different alkynes have been complexed or to those in which the chemistry of the coordinated alkyne has been studied to some extent.

Almost all acetylene complexes have been prepared by one of two methods: ligand substitution [Eq. (1)] or reductive complexation [Eq. (2)].

$$M-L + RC \equiv CR^1 \xrightarrow[h\nu]{\Delta \text{ or}} M-\underset{C}{\overset{C}{\mathrm{|||}}} \underset{R^1}{\overset{R}{<}} + L \qquad (1)$$

$$MX_2 + RC \equiv CR^1 \xrightarrow{2e^-} M-\underset{C}{\overset{C}{\mathrm{|||}}} \underset{R^1}{\overset{R}{<}} + 2X^- \qquad (2)$$

Ligand substitution is by far the most common method, proceeding thermally in some cases and photochemically in others, with carbon monoxide being the ligand most often replaced. The reductive method has been limited largely to the preparation of Group VIII complexes. The yields from either route vary widely and few attempts have been made to improve or optimize them. This certainly is one area in which further development is required in order to enhance the attractiveness of these complexes as synthetic intermediates.

TABLE 1

Preparation of Transition Metal–Alkyne Complexes

Transition metal starting material	Product complex	Typical yields, %	Reference
$(\eta^5-C_5H_5)M(CO)_4/h\nu$ (M = V, Nb)	$(\eta^5-C_5H_5)M(CO)_3(RC_2R)$	15–80	Tsumura and Hagihara, 1965
$(\eta^5-C_5H_5)M(CO)_4/h\nu$ (M = Nb, Ta)	$(\eta^5-C_5H_5)M(CO)_2(RC_2R)_2$	40–85	Nesmeyanov et al., 1969a,b
$(\eta^5-C_5H_5)_2MH_3$ (M = Nb, Ta)	$(\eta^5-C_5H_5)_2MH(RC_2R)$	—	Labinger and Schwartz, 1975; Labinger et al., 1974
$(\eta^5-C_5H_5)Cr(CO)_2NO/h\nu$	$(\eta^5-C_5H_5)Cr(CO)NO(RC_2R)$	10–40	Herberhold et al., 1976
$(\eta^5-C_5H_5)_2M(CO)/h\nu$ or $(\eta^5-C_5H_5)_2MCl_2/Na-Hg$ (M = Mo, W)	$(\eta^5-C_5H_5)_2M(RC_2R)$	> 90	Wong et al., 1974 Thomas, 1973
$(CH_3CN)_3W(CO)_3$	$(RC_2R)_3W(CO)$	15–50	Tate et al., 1963, 1964
$(\eta^5-C_5H_5)_2Mo_2(CO)_4$	$(\eta^5-C_5H_5)_2Mo_2(CO)_4(RC_2R)$	60–70	Klinger et al., 1975; Nakamura and Hagihara, 1963
$(\eta^5-C_5H_5)Mn(CO)_3/h\nu$	$(\eta^5-C_5H_5)Mn(CO)_2(RC_2R)$	—	Strohmeier and von Hobe, 1961; Boston et al., 1963
$(\eta^5-C_5H_5)Fe(CO)_2SnPh_3$	$(\eta^5-C_5H_5)Fe(CO)SnPh_3(RC_2R)$	—	Nesmeyanov et al., 1971

$Ru_3(CO)_{12}$	$Ru_4(CO)_{12}(RC_2R)$	5–10	Johnson et al., 1975
$NO(CO)L_2Os(Me_2CO)^+$	$NO(CO)L_2Os(RC_2R)^+$	—	Segal and Johnson, 1975
$(\eta^5-C_5H_5)Co(PPh_3)_2$	$(\eta^5-C_5H_5)Co(PPh_3)(RC_2R)$	60–80	Wakatsuki et al., 1974a
$Co_2(CO)_8$	$Co_2(CO)_6(RC_2R)$	60–90	Dickson and Fraser, 1974
$Co_4(CO)_{12}$	$Co_4(CO)_{10}(RC_2R)$	10–65	Dickson and Fraser, 1974
$(Ph_3P)_3RhCl$	$(Ph_3P)_2RhCl(RC_2R)$	84–99	Müller and Segnitz, 1973
$Rh_2(PF_3)_8$	$Rh_2(PF_3)_6(RC_2R)$	—	Bennett et al., 1972
$(Ph_3P)_2Ir(Cl)L$ $(L = N_2, CO)$	$(Ph_3P)_2IrCl(RC_2R)$	65–90	Cramer and Parshall, 1965; Collman and Kang, 1967
$[(\eta^5-C_5H_5)_2Ni(CO)]_2$	$(\eta^5-C_5H_5)_2Ni_2(RC_2R)$	35–85	Boston et al., 1962; Tilney-Bassett, 1961
$(Ph_3P)_2MX_2/e^-$ $(M = Pd, Pt; e^- = Zn, Na, N_2H_4)$ or $M(PPh_3)_4$	$(Ph_3P)_2M(RC_2R)$	50–90	Hartley, 1969
L_2PtX_2/Ag^+ $(L = PPh_2Me, X = Cl, CH_3)$	$L_2PtX(RC_2R)^+$	ca. 60	Chisholm and Clark, 1971
$L_2CuAlCl_4$ $(L = arene)$	$(RC_2R)CuAlCl_4^-$	—	Chukhadzhyan et al., 1976
$AuCl$	$(RC_2R)AuCl$	70–90	Hüttel and Forkl, 1972
$AuCl_3$	$(RC_2R)Au^+AuCl_4^-$	60–80	Hüttel and Forkl, 1972

B. Benzyne, Cycloalkyne, and Complexes of Other Reactive Alkynes

An important use of transition metal complexation has been in the stabilization of reactive molecules including cyclobutadiene, trimethylenemethane, o-xylylene, carbenes, carbynes, and others. In many cases, release of the ligand by chemical means has proven possible, making the complexed precursors valuable as shelf-stable sources of the reactive species for structural study or synthetic deployment. There also has been considerable interest in analogous complexes of benzyne, other strained cycloalkynes, and highly reactive acetylenes.

Both methods [Eqs. (1) and (2)] involve direct reaction with the alkyne to be complexed. However, when the alkyne itself is unstable or highly reactive, e.g., a strained cycloalkyne or benzyne, in situ generation and trapping can be employed. Since such complexes are interesting as potential sources of these theoretically significant molecules, we shall discuss their preparation in more detail.

The synthetic approach most commonly employed in attempts to prepare such complexes has involved generation of the reactive species from a suitable precursor in the presence of a transition metal complex which serves as the trapping agent. As an example, Bennett and co-workers reductively dehalogenated 1,2-dibromocyclohex- and -heptene in the presence of $Pt(PPh_3)_3$ to produce the corresponding cyclohexyne and cycloheptyne complexes, respectively (Bennett et al., 1971) [Eq. (3)]. The generally observed nonlin-

$$Pt(PPh_3)_3 \; + \; \overset{Br}{\underset{Br}{\bigg\langle}}\bigcirc(CH_2)_n \xrightarrow{\text{Na/Hg}} (Ph_3P)_2Pt - |||\;\bigcirc(CH_2)_n \qquad (3)$$

$$n = 4, 59\%$$
$$n = 5, 63\%$$

earity of the coordinated alkyne unit also was found in the cyclohexyne complex, which indicates that much of the strain associated with the cycloalkyne is relieved upon complexation (Robertson and Whimp, 1971).

$$\overset{Ph_3P}{\underset{Ph_3P}{\bigg\rangle}} Pt - |||\; \bigcirc{\scriptstyle 128°}$$

1.28 Å

These complexes are extremely stable, resisting displacement of the cyclohexyne and cycloheptyne by several donor ligands with the exception of perfluoro-2-butyne. While the alkyne was displaced in this case, its fate, unfortunately, was not determined. Further studies regarding the regeneration of these strained alkynes from their complexes is certainly warranted. Cyclooctyne, which is itself isolable, but is also fairly strained and highly reactive, has been complexed by direct reaction with $Pt(PPh_3)_4$ (Gilchrist *et al.*, 1968) [Eq. (4)].

$$Pt(PPh_3)_4 \; + \; \text{(cyclooctyne)} \xrightarrow[\text{(70\%)}]{\text{benzene}} (Ph_3P)_2Pt\text{—(cyclooctyne)} \qquad (4)$$

Dicobalt octacarbonyl has been found to react with perfluorocyclohexa-1,3-diene under pressure to produce the cyclohexeneyne complex **(I)** (Bailey *et al.*, 1964; Hunt and Wilkinson, 1965). The corresponding reaction with

$$Co_2(CO)_8 \; + \; \text{(perfluorocyclohexadiene)} \xrightarrow[\text{(15\%)}]{80°} \text{(cyclohexeneyne complex)} \qquad (5)$$

$(CO)_3Co \longrightarrow Co(CO)_3$

(I)

diiodobenzene failed to produce any benzyne complexes. No attempts to release the alkyne from **I** were reported.

Attempts to prepare benzyne complexes by the reactions of metal complexes with established benzyne precursors have been uniformly unsuccessful. In some cases, complexes derived from only partial decomposition of the precursors have been obtained (Cook and Jauhal, 1968). An earlier claim of the preparation of a nickel–benzyne complex by the reaction of $Ni(CO)_4$ and diiodobenzene (Gowling *et al.*, 1968) has been shown more recently to be erroneous (Bailey *et al.*, 1971). The reactions between C_6F_5MgBr and several metal carbonyls have been studied briefly (Roe and Massey, 1970). In the reaction with $Co_2(CO)_8$, a complex of stoichiometry (alkyne)$Co_4(CO)_{10}$ was obtained which underwent thermolysis to give perfluorofluorenone.

$$Co_2(CO)_8 \; + \; C_6F_5MgBr \longrightarrow Co_4(CO)_{10}(C_6F_4) \qquad (6)$$

This product, which is comparable to the cyclopentadienones produced in the thermal reactions of (alkyne)$Co_4(CO)_{10}$, suggests that the intermediate may be a tetrafluorobenzyne complex.

To date, the only proved examples of benzyne complexes have come, oddly enough, from the reactions of aryl phosphines and arsines with $Os_3(CO)_{12}$ (Bradford *et al.*, 1972; Deeming *et al.*, 1973). Among the nine products isolated from the reaction of $Os_3(CO)_{12}$ with PPh_3 was the complex (II). Similar complexes have been characterized from the reaction of

$$Os_3(CO)_{12} + PPh_3 \xrightarrow[\text{xylene}]{\Delta} \quad (7)$$

$$(CO)_3Os \underset{\substack{ \\ Os \leftarrow PPh_2 \\ (Co)_2}}{\overset{\substack{PPh_2}}{\underset{\longleftarrow}{\longleftarrow}}} Os(CO)_2$$

$$(II)$$

$Os_3(CO)_{12}$ with $PPhMe_2$ and $AsPhMe_2$. Release of the ligand from these complexes was not discussed. In view of the expense of osmium compounds and the complex mixtures produced from these reactions, these complexes are rather unattractive synthetically as benzyne sources.

Recently, the highly reactive dimethoxyacetylene has been trapped at low temperature upon treatment with dicobalt octacarbonyl (Messeguer *et al.*,

$$\underset{H}{\overset{CH_3O}{\diagdown}} C = C \underset{OCH_3}{\overset{Cl}{\diagup}} \xrightarrow[-60°]{NaNH_2} [CH_3OC \equiv COCH_3] \xrightarrow{Co_2(CO)_8} \underset{\substack{| \\ Co_2(CO)_6}}{CH_3OC \equiv COCH_3} \quad (8)$$

1973) [Eq. (8)]. The high reactivity of cobalt carbonyl toward alkynes foreshadows its future wider use for complexing other highly reactive alkynes.

IV. REACTIONS OF ALKYNE COMPLEXES

A. Reactions in Which the Coordinated Triple Bond Is Unaffected

An extension of the use of metal complexes to stabilize reactive intermediates is their utilization to deactivate reactive functional groups and hence to serve as protective groups. The propensity of transition metals to form stable complexes with olefins and acetylenes renders them particularly well suited to serve as protecting groups for carbon–carbon unsaturation.

The dicobalt hexacarbonyl unit has been found to fulfill the three essential criteria of a protecting group for the carbon–carbon triple bond, namely (1) ease of introduction and removal; (2) stability under conditions which effect reaction at the unprotected functionality; and (3) inexpensiveness or recyclability. (Alkyne) Co_2 $(CO)_6$ complexes can be prepared in good yield by the reaction of alkynes with dicobalt octacarbonyl (Dickson and Fraser, 1974; Sternberg *et al.*, 1954) [Eq. (9)]. A wide variety of functionality is tolerated in

$$R-C \equiv C-R' + Co_2(CO)_8 \xrightarrow[(70-90\%)]{25°} \underset{(CO)_3Co-\!\!-Co(CO)_3}{\overset{R'}{\underset{}{C}}\!\!\equiv\!\!\overset{R}{C}} + 2Co \qquad (9)$$

the alkyne including hydroxyl, carbonyl, carboalkoxy, halogen (but not in the α position) (Tirpak *et al.*, 1960), and amino groups. Dickson and Fraser (1974) list $-Co_2(CO)_6$ complexes of over 150 alkynes, easily making these the most plentiful of all metal–acetylene complexes.

The coordinated alkyne linkage in these species has been found to be relatively unreactive towards electrophilic reagents which attack the free triple bond. Whereas Friedel-Crafts acylation of arylacetylenes is complicated by attack at the triple bond, Seyferth and co-workers have shown that the corresponding cobalt complexes undergo selective acylation on the aromatic ring (Seyferth and Wehman, 1970; Seyferth *et al.*, 1975c). Representative examples are shown.

$$\text{(structure: aryl–C}\equiv\text{C–aryl with Co}_2(\text{CO})_6) \xrightarrow[\text{10AlCl}_3]{\text{2CH}_3\text{COCl}} \text{CH}_3\text{CO–}(\text{structure})\text{–COCH}_3 \qquad (13)$$

$$(88\%)$$

With a variety of substituted arylacetylenes, mixtures of mono- and disubstituted products were obtained in combined yields of 60–90%, while diacylation was effected in high yield using an excess of acylating agent. The modified alkynes were readily recovered upon treatment of the complexes with ceric ion:

$$\underset{\underset{\text{Co}_2(\text{CO})_6}{|}}{\text{CH}_3\text{COC}_6\text{H}_4\text{—}\equiv\text{—C}_6\text{H}_5} \xrightarrow[\text{acetone/H}_2\text{O}]{(\text{NH}_4)_2\text{Ce(NO}_3)_6} \text{CH}_3\text{COC}_6\text{H}_4\text{—}\equiv\text{—C}_6\text{H}_5 \qquad (14)$$

$$(75\%)$$

Yields for this process were uniformly in the 70–90% range.

Nicholas and Pettit (1971) have used the cobalt carbonyl protecting group to effect selective addition reactions to the double bond of ene–yne complexes. For example, the 1-octene-4-yne complex underwent smooth reduction at the double bond when treated with diimide. Similar reductions also

$$\underset{\underset{\text{Co}_2(\text{CO})_6}{|}}{(\text{structure})} \xrightarrow[(92\%)]{\text{N}_2\text{H}_2} \underset{\underset{\text{Co}_2(\text{CO})_6}{|}}{(\text{structure})} \qquad (15)$$

were accomplished by hydroboration/protonolysis as in Eq. (16). The ene–yne–ol complex (III) could be hydrated by hydroboration/oxidation. Cleavage of the intermediate borane with molecular oxygen is preferred since significant decomposition was observed using the more common basic peroxide method. Whereas acid-catalyzed hydration of ene–ynes generally re-

$$(\text{steroid structure}) \xrightarrow[\substack{2.\ \text{HOAc} \\ (60\%)}]{1.\ \text{BH}_3\cdot\text{THF}} (\text{steroid structure}) \qquad (16)$$

$$\underset{\underset{\text{Co}_2(\text{CO})_6}{|}}{(\text{structure})} \xrightarrow[\substack{2.\ \text{H}_2\text{O}_2/\text{OH}^- \\ (45\%)}]{1.\ \text{BH}_3\cdot\text{THF}} \underset{\underset{\text{Co}_2(\text{CO})_6}{|}}{(\text{structure})} \qquad (17)$$

(III)

sults in preferential reaction at the triple bond (Johnson, 1946), the complex **(III)**, upon treatment with HBF_4/acetic anhydride followed by aqueous workup, produced the corresponding complexed acetylenic diol. The facility of this reaction, compared to that of the free ligand, provided preliminary evidence that carbonium ions adjacent to the $(alkynyl)Co_2(CO)_6$ moiety possess unusual stability. Further investigations of this phenomenon and its synthetic applicability will be discussed subsequently.

$$(18)$$

The transformed alkynes in the previous study were readily recovered by oxidation of the complexes with alcoholic ferric nitrate. Representative examples are shown in Eqs. (18) and (19). The alkynes in the cobalt com-

$$(19)$$

$$(20)$$

plexes also may be displaced by more electron deficient alkynes such as $CF_3C{\equiv}CCF_3$ and $RO_2CC{\equiv}CCO_2R$ (Cetini *et al.*, 1967). This ligand exchange reaction has not been exploited for synthetic purposes, however.

We have discussed several examples in which the triple bond has been deactivated through complexation. While complexation may diminish reactivity at the site of coordination, this process may enhance reactivity at other positions in the ligand. Thus it has now been shown that complexed propargylic cations **(IV)** exhibit marked stability. In an early study reflecting

$$R'-\!\!\!\equiv\!\!\!-\overset{+}{C}\!\!\overset{R^2}{\underset{R^3}{\diagdown}} \quad \textbf{(IV)}$$
$$\underset{Co_2(CO)_6}{|}$$

this stability, propargylic–alcohol complexes were found to readily undergo mild acid-catalyzed dehydration to the corresponding conjugated ene–yne complexes (Nicholas and Pettit, 1972) [Eqs. (21) and (22)]. Dehydration of

$$(21)$$

$$(22)$$

free tertiary propargylic alcohols generally requires more forcing conditions and is sometimes accompanied by propargylic-allenic rearrangement.

French workers have extended this reaction to develop a stereoselective synthesis of E–ene–ynes (Descoins and Samain, 1976). Whereas cyclopropyl alkynyl carbinols gave mixtures of ene–ynes of variable isomeric composition under acidic conditions, the corresponding cobalt complexes yielded the E isomers almost exclusively after oxidative decomplexation. Yields for the three step sequence were good. The enhanced selectivity presumably is a result of the steric demand of the cobalt carbonyl moiety. The conjugated ene–ynes are useful intermediates in the preparation of insect pheromones, several of which contain the E,Z-diene unit.

$$(23)$$

$$(24)$$

90–99% E (53–65% overall yield)

Several salts of these cobalt-stabilized carbonium ions have recently been isolated (Connor and Nicholas, 1977) [Eq. (25)]. ^{1}H nmr and ir studies

$$
\begin{array}{c}
\equiv\!\!-\!\!\overset{R^1}{\underset{\underset{Co_2(CO)_6}{R^2}}{<}}\!\!-OH
\quad\longrightarrow\quad
\equiv\!\!-\!\!\overset{R^1}{\underset{\underset{Co_2(CO)_6}{R^2}}{<}}\!\!\oplus \quad Z^{\ominus}
\end{array}
\qquad (25)
$$

a: $R^1 = R^2 = Ph$; $Z = SbF_6$
b: $R^1 = R^2 = Me$; $Z = SbF_6$
c: $R^1 = Me$, $R^2 = H$; $Z = BF_4$
d: $R^1 = R^2 = H$; $Z = BF_4$

indicate extensive charge dispersal onto the (ethynyl)Co$_2$(CO)$_6$ moiety and their formulation as carbonium ions is, therefore, not strictly accurate. The pK_R^+ values of the cations, which reflect their thermodynamic stability, do not depend significantly on the nature of R^1 and R^2 and were found to be about -7. The cations, therefore, are approximately as stable as the triphenylmethyl cation.

Exploratory studies are under way to assess the utility of these complexes as alkylating agents. Of particular interest are their reactions with carbon nucleophiles such as reactive aromatics and enol derivatives. In model studies with anisole, the cationic complexes, used directly or generated *in situ* from the corresponding carbinols, reacted rapidly under mild conditions to give the alkylated aromatics in high yields (R. Lockwood and K. M. Nicholas, 1977). The reaction of the dimethyl ethynyl complex is perhaps most

$$
\begin{array}{c}
\equiv\!\!-\!\!\overset{R^1}{\underset{\underset{(CO)_6}{Co_2}}{<}}\!\!-OH
\quad\xrightarrow[\substack{HBF_4\cdot Me_2O\\0^\circ}]{C_6H_5OCH_3}\quad
\equiv\!\!-\!\!\overset{R^1}{\underset{\underset{(CO)_6}{Co_2}}{<}}\!\!-\!\!\bigcirc\!\!-OCH_3 \\[2em]
+\quad
\equiv\!\!-\!\!\overset{R^1}{\underset{\underset{(CO)_6}{Co_2}}{<}}\!\!-\!\!\overset{OCH_3}{\bigcirc}
\end{array}
\qquad (26)
$$

b: $R^1 = R^2 = Me$ (78% *p*)
c: $R^1 = Me$ (53% *p* + 25% *o*)
d: $R^1 = R^2 = H$ (47% *p* + 35% *o*)

significant since it demonstrates that quaternary centers are easily generated by this method. The overall scheme outlined in Eq. (27) thus provides a new method for the introduction of the versatile carbon–carbon triple bond. The reaction of acetylacetone with the monomethyl complex (H. D. Hodes and

$$R^1\!\!-\!\!\equiv\!\!-\!\!\overset{OH}{\underset{R^3}{\overset{|}{C}}}\!\!R^2 \xrightarrow[\substack{2.\ H^+,\ :C\diagdown \\ 3.\ Fe^{3+}}]{1.\ Co_2(CO)_8} R^1\!\!-\!\!\equiv\!\!-\!\!\overset{\overset{|}{\underset{\diagdown}{C}}}{\underset{R^3}{\overset{|}{C}}}\!\!R^2 \qquad (27)$$

K. M. Nicholas, unpublished results) provides encouragement that similar alkylations of enolic compounds will be successful.

$$\underset{\substack{Co_2 \\ (CO)_6}}{\equiv}\!\!\diagup\!\!\overset{CH_3}{\underset{OH}{<}} \xrightarrow[\substack{(62\%)}]{CH_3COCH_2COCH_3} \underset{\substack{Co_2 \\ (CO)_6}}{\equiv}\!\!-\!\!\overset{\displaystyle H_3C\!-\!\overset{O}{\diagup}}{\underset{CH_3}{<}}\!\!\overset{O}{\diagdown}\!\!CH_3 \qquad (28)$$

B. Reactions Which Occur at the Coordinated Triple Bond

1. Reactions with Electrophiles

Alkyne complexes of low oxidation state metals react with electrophiles generally to produce alkene derivatives resulting from addition of the electrophilic species to the coordinated triple bond. These reactions often proceed by way of σ-vinyl–metal derivatives, and in several cases such intermediates have been isolated. The vinyl complexes, in turn, may be cleaved in a subsequent reaction to afford substituted alkenes [Eq. (29)].

$$M\!\!-\!\!\overset{R}{\underset{R}{\diagup}}\!\!\overset{\delta+\quad\delta-}{|||}\xrightarrow{A-B} M\diagup\overset{R}{\underset{B}{\diagdown}}\overset{R}{\underset{A}{\diagdown}}\xrightarrow{A-B}\overset{R}{\underset{R}{\diagup}}\overset{A}{\underset{A}{\diagdown}} + MB_2 \qquad (29)$$

The interaction of alkyne complexes with protic acids has been the most thoroughly studied of electrophilic reactions. When these reactions proceed to organic products, alkenes are formed, often stereospecifically. Schwartz and co-workers have studied the reactions of Cp_2MH(alkyne) complexes of the early transition metals, Ta (Labinger *et al.*, 1974) and Nb (Labinger and Schwartz, 1975). These complexes gave cis alkenes exclusively in nearly quantitative yield when treated with strong acids, as exemplified by the formation of *cis*-2-octene from the tantalum–octyne complex. Since the

$$\text{Cp}_2\text{TaH}(\text{PrC}_2\text{Pr}) \xrightarrow{\text{HBF}_4} \qquad\qquad (30)$$

(M = Ta, Nb)

acetylene complexes are easily synthesized (Labinger and Schwartz, 1975; Labinger et al., 1974), this reaction may prove to be of some synthetic value.

The related cyclopentadienylmolybdenum complexes appear to have similar reactivity. The 2-butyne complex thus gave cis-2-butene as the only organic product upon treatment with hydrogen chloride at low temperature (Thomas, 1973). The generality of this reaction has not been demonstrated.

$$\text{Cp}_2\text{Mo}(\text{CH}_3\text{C}_2\text{CH}_3) \xrightarrow[\text{H}_2\text{O},\ -78°]{\text{HCl}} \qquad\qquad (31)$$

The reactions of zerovalent platinum–alkyne complexes with acids have been studied by several groups (Barlex et al., 1969; Mann et al., 1971; Tripathy and Roundhill, 1970; Kemmitt et al., 1973). When one equivalent of acid is employed, it is possible to isolate the σ-vinyl derivatives. Nmr studies have generally indicated a cis arrangement about the double bond (Mann et al., 1971), presumably resulting from initial protonation of the metal, followed by cis M—H addition. The yields for this first step were uniformly good. Shaw and co-workers have reported that addition to ter-

$$\text{L}_2\text{Pt}\!-\!\!\!\begin{array}{c}\text{R}\\ \|\|\\ \text{R}\end{array} \xrightarrow[(70-90\%)]{\text{HX}} \text{L}_2\text{XPt} \qquad\qquad (32)$$

L = PR$_3$, AsR$_3$
HX = HCl, HBr, CF$_3$CO$_2$H

minal alkynes proceeds in the Markovnikov sense as shown in Eq. (33) (Mann et al., 1971).

$$L_2Pt-\underset{H}{\overset{R}{|||}} \xrightarrow{HX} L_2Pt\underset{H}{\overset{R}{\diagup}}H \qquad (33)$$

(R = Me, Et, Ph, Tol)

The further reaction of these platinum complexes with an excess of acid to afford alkenes has received much less attention. If the alkyne bears the strongly electron-withdrawing trifluoromethyl group, the intermediate vinyl species is resistant to further electrophilic cleavage (Kemmitt et al., 1973). The diphenylacetylene complex, on the other hand, reacted with excess HCl to product trans-stilbene in almost quantitative yield (Tripathy and Round-hill, 1970). The corresponding 2-butyne complex gave a 1:4 mixture (the thermodynamic ratio) of cis and trans butenes under similar conditions. It is

$$(Ph_3P)_2Pt-\underset{Ph}{\overset{Ph}{|||}} \xrightarrow[TFA]{excess\ HCl\ or} \underset{Ph}{\overset{H}{\diagdown}}\underset{H}{\overset{Ph}{\diagup}} + (Ph_3P)_2PtX_2 \qquad (34)$$

$$(Ph_3P)_2Pt-\underset{CH_3}{\overset{CH_3}{|||}} \xrightarrow{TFA} \underset{H_3C}{\overset{H}{\diagdown}}\underset{H}{\overset{CH_3}{\diagup}} + \underset{H}{\overset{H}{\diagdown}}\underset{CH_3}{\overset{CH_3}{\diagup}} + (Ph_3P)_2PtX_2 \qquad (35)$$

$$4:1$$

not clear whether the predominance of trans alkenes in these cases reflects the stereochemistry of the cleavage of the vinyl complexes or whether isomerization of the olefins occurs under the reaction conditions.

Rhodium(I) and iridium(I)–hexafluorobutyne complexes also can be protonated to form σ-vinyl complexes (Kemmitt et al., 1973) [Eqs. (36) and (37)]. The preparation of alkenes from these has not been reported.

$$(Ph_3P)_2Ir(CO)Cl(CF_3C_2CF_3) \xrightarrow[CH_2Cl_2]{TFA} (Ph_3P)_2(CO)ClIr\underset{H}{\overset{CF_3}{\diagup}}\overset{CF_3}{\diagdown} \qquad (36)$$

$$(Ph_3P)_2RhCl(CF_3C_2CF_3) \xrightarrow[Et_2O]{HCl} (Ph_3P)_2ClRh\underset{H}{\overset{CF_3}{\diagup}}\overset{CF_3}{\diagdown} \qquad (37)$$

$$(70\%)$$

The behavior of $(alkyne)Co_2(CO)_6$ and $(alkyne)Co_4(CO)_{10}$ toward acids depends markedly on the nature of the alkyne. In both systems with the internal acetylene tolane, *trans*-stilbene was reported to be the only product obtained upon treatment with acidic methanol [Eqs. (38) and (39)] (Krüerke

$$(PhC_2Ph)Co_2(CO)_6 \xrightarrow[\;(15\%)\;]{H_2SO_4/MeOH} \quad \substack{H \qquad Ph \\ \diagdown \qquad \diagup \\ \\ \diagup \qquad \diagdown \\ Ph \qquad H} \qquad (38)$$

$$(PhC_2Ph)Co_4(CO)_{10} \xrightarrow[\;(89\%)\;]{H_2SO_4/MeOH} \quad \substack{H \qquad Ph \\ \diagdown \qquad \diagup \\ \\ \diagup \qquad \diagdown \\ Ph \qquad H} \qquad (39)$$

and Hübel, 1961). Extension of these reactions to other internal acetylenes deserves some attention because of the ready availability of the complexes. Terminal alkyne complexes, $(RC_2H)Co_2(CO)_6$, under similar conditions, produce the cluster complexes **(V)** (Markby *et al.*, 1958). Since these compounds are derived from acetylene complexes and because their organic chemistry has been extensively investigated, we shall discuss their reactions in more detail in Section V.

$$(RC_2H)Co_2(CO)_6 \xrightarrow[\Delta]{H_2SO_4/MeOH} \quad (CO)_3Co \substack{CH_2R \\ | \\ C \\ \diagup | \diagdown \\ --|-- \\ \diagdown | \diagup \\ Co \\ (CO)_3} Co(CO)_3 \qquad (40)$$

$$(V)$$

Few reports on the reactions of alkyne complexes with electrophiles other than protic acids have appeared. Bromine has been found to react with a few systems to afford vicinal dibromoalkenes [e.g., Eqs. (41) and (42)] (Krüerke and Hübel, 1961; Hübel and Merenyi, 1964). These reactions may, in fact, involve bromine addition subsequent to oxidative release of the ligand from the metal. The platinum dicyanoacetylene complex behaves differently in forming a product in which addition has occurred but the complex has remained intact (McClure and Baddley, 1970).

$$(PhC_2Ph)Co_4(CO)_{10} \xrightarrow[\;(60\%)\;]{Br_2} \quad \substack{Br \qquad Ph \\ \diagdown \qquad \diagup \\ \\ \diagup \qquad \diagdown \\ Ph \qquad Br} \qquad (41)$$

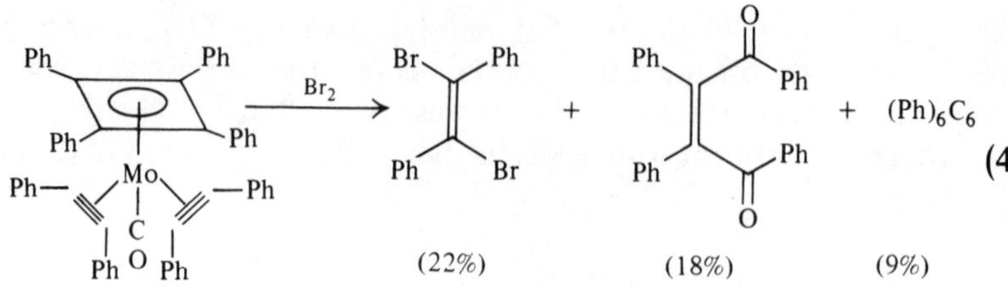

$$(42)$$

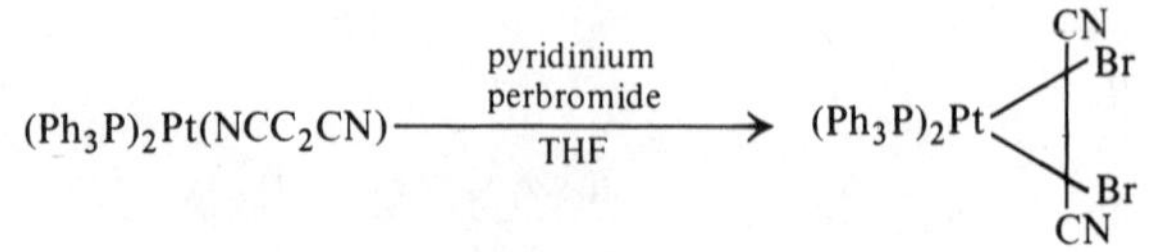

$$(43)$$

Halomercuration of the platinum perfluorobutyne complex has been reported to give adducts with the cis arrangement about the vinyl group

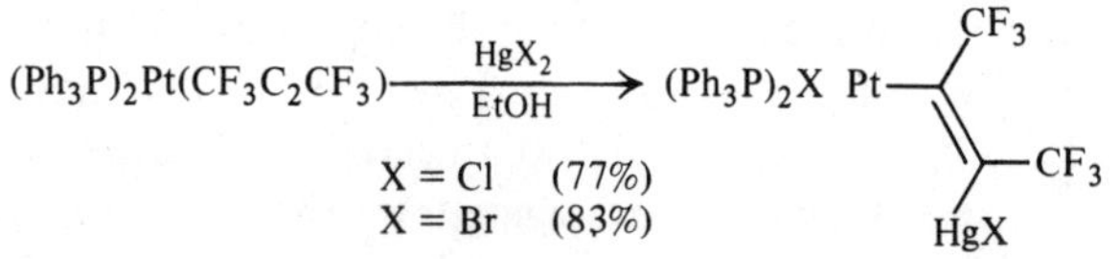

$$(44)$$

$$
\begin{array}{ll}
X = Cl & (77\%) \\
X = Br & (83\%)
\end{array}
$$

(Kemmitt *et al.*, 1973). Further transformations of the σ-complexes were not discussed.

In one case, electrophilic substitution at the coordinated triple bond has been demonstrated. The dicobalt–hexacarbonyl complexes below [Eqs. (45) and (46)] undergo acylation, albeit rather inefficiently, in a process which is undoubtedly facilitated by the susceptibility of the C—Sn bond to electrophilic attack (Seyferth and White, 1971).

$$(Me_3CC_2SnMe_3)Co_2(CO)_6 \xrightarrow[AlCl_3]{CH_3COCl} (Me_3CC_2\overset{\overset{\displaystyle O}{\|}}{C}CH_3)Co_2(CO)_6 \quad (45)$$
$$(12\%)$$

$$(HC_2SnMe_3)Co_2(CO)_6 \xrightarrow[AlCl_3]{CH_3COCl} (HC_2\overset{\overset{\displaystyle O}{\|}}{C}CH_3)Co_2(CO)_6 \quad (46)$$
$$(20\%)$$

2. Reactions with Nucleophiles

Alkynes coordinated to transition metals in their higher oxidation states, e.g., Pt(II), or in cationic complexes, often are prone to attack by nucleophiles, in analogy to the well-known and synthetically important Hg(II)-catalyzed hydration of alkynes. Overall cis or trans addition may be envisioned, depending upon whether the nucleophile first coordinates to the metal or rather attacks the alkyne externally.

$$
\text{M}-\overset{\displaystyle R}{\underset{\displaystyle R}{\text{|||}}} \; + \; :\text{Nu} \longrightarrow \; \text{M}-\overset{\displaystyle R}{\underset{\displaystyle \text{Nu}\ \ R}{\text{|||}}} \longrightarrow \; \text{M}\overset{\displaystyle R}{\underset{\displaystyle \text{Nu}}{\diagup\!\!\backslash\!\!-R}}
\tag{47}
$$

$$
\text{M}-\overset{\displaystyle R}{\underset{\displaystyle R}{\text{|||}}} \; + \; :\text{Nu} \longrightarrow \; \text{M}\overset{\displaystyle R}{\underset{\displaystyle R}{\diagdown\!\!\diagup\!\!-\text{Nu}}}
\tag{48}
$$

Chisolm, Clark, and co-workers have studied extensively the chemistry of cationic Pt(II) complexes of type **(VI)** (for review, see Chisholm and Clark, 1973). The products obtained from the reactions of nucleophiles with these complexes are dependent on the alkyne, associated ligands, and the solvent, and have been interpreted in terms of a carbonium ion model. In the case of

$$
\underset{\substack{\text{(VI)}\\ (L = PMePh_2, AsMe_2Ph)}}{L_2(CH_3)Pt \overset{+}{\ }\overset{\diagup C \diagdown R^1}{\underset{\diagdown C \diagup R^2}{\text{|||}}}}
\overset{\substack{CH_3OH\\ R_1, R_2\\ = \text{alkyl, aryl}}}{\xrightarrow{\hspace{1cm}}}
L_2(CH_3)Pt \overset{\displaystyle R^1}{\underset{\displaystyle R^2}{\diagup\!\!\backslash\!\!-OMe}}
\tag{49}
$$

$$
\xrightarrow{R_2 = H} [L_2(CH_3)Pt\!-\!\overset{+}{C}\!=\!CHR^1]
$$

$$
\xrightarrow[CH_3OH]{} L_2(CH_3)Pt = C\overset{\diagup CH_2R^1}{\diagdown OCH_3}
$$

internal alkynes, the σ-vinyl ether derivatives were obtained in good yield, the rate of reaction being strongly influenced by the electron-attracting ability of R^1 and R^2. Complexes of terminal acetylenes generally are not isolable, but alkoxycarbene complexes are formed instead. The latter arise, most likely, via attack of alcohol on the intermediate platinum-stabilized carbonium ion. The cationic complexes **(VI)** probably also are intermediates in the reactions of $L_2Pt(CH_3)Cl$ with acetylenes, which, in alcohol solvents, produce similar products.

The related o-benzoquinone–Pt(II) complex has been observed to react with diethylamine to give an enamine derivative (Barlex *et al.*, 1972). The stereochemistry was not determined. Practical methods for regenerating

$$(50)$$

organic compounds from these various platinum complexes have not been developed. Electrophilic cleavage of the vinyl ether and enamine complexes might provide a route to carbonyl compounds. Economic considerations require that the platinum-containing products from such reactions be recyclable.

Nucleophilic attack by a carbanion on a rhodium–acetylene complex has been postulated in the reaction of tolane with MeMgBr in the presence of $(Ph_3P)_3RhBr$ (Michman and Balog, 1971). This interpretation is supported by the known formation of rhodium–alkyne complexes under these conditions (Müller and Segnitz, 1973) and by the predominant formation of *trans*-α-methyl-stilbene. Additional study of the scope of this reaction would seem worthwhile since recycling of the rhodium-containing by-product, $(Ph_3P)_3RhOH$, should be possible.

$$(51)$$

Lastly, the decompositions of the Au(I) complexes **(VII)** and **(VIII)** yield a variety of interesting products, some of which probably arise from halide attack on the coordinated ligand (Hüttel and Forkl, 1972). In chloroform solution, complex **(VII)** gave a mixture of *trans*-dichlorobutene, substituted butadienes, and cyclobutenes in modest overall yield. The neutral butyne

$$(52)$$

complex produced *cis-* and *trans*-dichlorobutenes and 2,3-dichlorobuta-dienes [Eq. (48)]. Perhaps of greater synthetic interest was the observation

$$(MeC_2Me)AuCl \xrightarrow{\Delta} \text{(VIII)} \quad \begin{array}{c}Cl \\ \end{array}\begin{array}{c}Me \\ \end{array} + \begin{array}{c}Cl \\ \end{array}\begin{array}{c}Me \\ \end{array} + \begin{array}{c}Cl \quad Cl \\ Me \quad Me \\ Me \quad Me \end{array} \quad (53)$$

that $AuCl_3$ reacted with excess alkyne to produce substituted cyclobutenes as the only organic products. These latter reactions have analogies in Pd(II) chemistry to be discussed in Section IV,B,3c.

$$MeC \equiv CMe + AuCl_3 \longrightarrow \begin{array}{c} Me \quad Me \\ \quad Cl \\ \quad Me \\ Me \quad Cl \end{array} + (MeC_2Me)Au^+AuCl_4^- \quad (54)$$

$$PhC \equiv CPh + AuCl_3 \xrightarrow{(>75\%)} \begin{array}{c} Ph \quad Ph \\ \quad Cl \\ \quad Ph \\ Ph \quad Cl \end{array} + (MeC_2Me)Au^+AuCl_4^- \quad (55)$$

3. Insertion Reactions

The ligand migration or insertion reaction is a fundamental mechanistic process of organometallic chemistry. As relating to acetylene complexes, it may be represented as shown in [Eq. (58)]. The reaction thus may be viewed either as an addition of M—L to the acetylene or, alternatively, as an insertion of the acetylene into the M—L bond. In cases where L = carbon monoxide, alkene, acetylene, or other potentially bidentate ligands, L may remain bonded to the metal, resulting in metallocycle formation [Eq. (57)].

$$\begin{array}{c} L \\ M \\ \|-R \\ R \end{array} \longrightarrow \begin{array}{c} L \\ M \quad R \\ R \end{array} \quad L = H, \text{alkyl} \quad (56)$$

$$\longrightarrow \begin{array}{c} L \\ M \quad R \\ R \end{array} \quad \begin{array}{l} L = CO, \text{alkene}, \\ \text{alkyne, RNC} \end{array} \quad (57)$$

Although catalytic reactions of alkynes typified by Eqs. (56) and (57) are myriad, the intermediacy of L—M—(alkyne) species generally has been presumed and not proved. The discussion here will primarily be limited to those examples in which such species have been isolated.

a. Metal Hydride Insertions. The addition of transition metal hydrides to carbon–carbon unsaturation constitutes a key step in many catalytic reactions, including homogeneous hydrogenation, hydroformylation, and isomerization. Although additions of metal hydrides to acetylenes have been reported to yield both cis and trans vinyl derivatives, in those cases in which the hydride–metal–alkyne complex has been isolated, cis addition generally has been observed as a stereospecific process. [Eq. (58)] (Clark and Wong, 1975; Clark *et al.*, 1975; Schwartz *et al.*, 1972).

$$M-H \ + \ RC \equiv CR \longrightarrow M \underset{\underset{R}{\overset{\|}{\underset{|}{\|}}}}{\overset{H}{\diagup}} -R \longrightarrow \overset{M}{\diagdown} \underset{R}{\overset{}{=}} \overset{H}{\diagup} R \qquad (58)$$

The synthetically most significant sequence which incorporates such a reaction has been reported by Schwartz and co-workers (1972). Treatment of alkynes with $(Ph_3P)_2(CO)RhH$ leads to the formation of cis vinyl complexes via an intermediate alkyne complex which can be isolated for $R^1 = CH_3$, $R^2 = CO_2CH_3$. The vinyl complexes undergo oxidative addi-

$$(PPh_3)_2(CO)RhH \ + \ R^1C \equiv CR^2 \longrightarrow (PPh_3)_2(CO)Rh(H) \, (R^1C \equiv CR^2)$$

$$\Big\uparrow \mathrm{NaBH_4} \qquad\qquad\qquad\qquad\qquad\qquad\qquad\qquad\qquad \Big\downarrow \qquad (59)$$

$$(Ph_3P)_2(CO)RhI \ + \ \underset{R^2}{\overset{R^1}{\diagdown}}\!\!\underset{H}{\overset{CH_3}{=}}\!\!\diagup \quad \xrightarrow[\Delta \atop (75\%)]{CH_3I} \quad (Ph_3P)_2(CO)Rh \diagup \underset{H}{\overset{R^1}{=}}\diagdown R^2$$

tion upon treatment with methyl iodide. Thermally induced reductive elimination occurs stereospecifically $(>98\%)$, affording dimethyl methylmaleate $(R^1 = R^2 = CO_2CH_3)$. Methyl propiolate was similarly converted to methyl β-methylcrotonate in good yield. The $L_2Rh(CO)I$ was reconvertible to the original hydride complex, thus permitting recycling.

In a related study, $Cp_2NbH(RC \equiv CR)$ complexes were found to undergo cis insertion when treated with carbon monoxide (Labinger and Schwartz,

$$Cp_2Nb\underset{\underset{R}{\overset{\|}{\underset{|}{\|}}}}{\overset{H}{\diagup}}-R \xrightarrow[75°]{CO} Cp_2Nb\underset{H}{\overset{CO}{\diagup}}\!\!\underset{R}{\overset{}{\diagdown}}R \xrightarrow{MeOSO_2F} \underset{H}{\overset{Me}{\diagdown}}\!\!\underset{R}{\overset{R}{=}}\!\!\diagup \quad \underset{R}{\overset{Me}{\diagdown}}\!\!\underset{H}{\overset{R}{=}}\!\!\diagup$$

$$(60)$$

1975). The vinyl complexes, however, produced mixtures of cis and trans alkenes.

Although the intermediacy of acetylene complexes has not been demonstrated in the hydrozirconation reaction developed by Schwartz (see Hart et al., 1975), the attractiveness of this process as an alternative to hydroboration warrants a brief discussion at this point. The zirconium–hydride complex, Cp_2ZrHCl, which is conveniently prepared (Hart and Schwartz, 1974) from Cp_2ZrCl_2 and $NaAlH_2(OCH_2CH_2OCH_3)_2$, rapidly adds to alkynes, affording cis vinyl derivatives (Booth and Lloyd, 1972). Although both modes of Zr–H addition to unsymmetrical alkynes occur, isomerization to the less hindered derivative is accomplished readily, resulting in higher selectivity than for simple hydroboration. Treatment of the

$$(61)$$

vinyl complexes with N-halosuccinimide gives vinyl halides in good yield. This latter step occurs with retention of configuration, permitting overall cis addition in the anti-Markovnikov sense.

The effects of variations in ligands and the coordination geometry of the metal on the facility of platinum hydride addition to acetylenes have been investigated. Both neutral and cationic complexes react at 25° with alkynes via π-complexed intermediates to produce vinyl complexes resulting from cis M–H addition (Clark et al., 1975). The orientation of addition is that

$$(62)$$

$$(63)$$

expected from M—H addition to a complexed alkyne with carbonium ion character. Further transformations of these vinyl derivatives were not reported.

In one unusual case, a dimethyl acetylenedicarboxylate complex, when heated, suffered ortho-metallation to yield a *trans*-σ-vinyl complex (Clark and Hine, 1976). Although this reaction is of little synthetic value, it does

$$(Ph_3P)_2Pt—\overset{CO_2CH_3}{\underset{CO_2CH_3}{|||}} \quad \xrightarrow[\text{(40\%)}]{130°} \quad Ph_2P——Pt— \overset{CO_2CH_3}{\underset{\underset{CO_2CH_3}{—H}}{}} \qquad (64)$$

indicate the possibility of trans addition of metal hydride from an acetylene complex, which is of some interest. The mechanism of this reaction is unknown. It may involve a bimolecular process similar to those proposed in the addition of $HMn(CO)_5$ and $HRe(CO)_5$ to acetylenes (Booth and Hargreaves, 1971). Alternatively, a concerted trans addition, as proposed by Nakamura (see Nakamura and Otsuka, 1972) for the addition of Cp_2-MoH_2, may be operative.

b. Metal Alkyl Insertions. The addition of metal alkyls to alkynes is potentially a route to trisubstituted olefins which are of value in natural product synthesis [Eq. (65)]. Established examples of such additions which

$$M-R^1 \; + \; R^2-\equiv-R^3 \xrightarrow{\quad} M \overset{R^1}{\underset{R^3}{\diagup\!\!\!\diagdown}} R^2 \xrightarrow{\quad} X \overset{R^1}{\underset{R^3}{\diagup\!\!\!\diagdown}} R^2 \qquad (65)$$

involve detectable complexed alkyne intermediates, however, are relatively rare.

The Pt(II)–acetylene complexes have been studied most thoroughly in this respect. Clark and his co-workers have considered the importance of the nature of the alkyne, the coordination geometry of the metal, ancillary ligands, etc., on the rate of M—R addition. In general, it appears that electron-deficient alkynes undergo addition more readily. Thus, it was observed that, whereas the diphenylacetylene complex (VIII) (R^1 = Ph), is stable in refluxing benzene for two days, the corresponding perfluoro-2-butyne and acetylenedicarboxylate complexes ($R^1 = CF_3$, CO_2Me) are not isolable but are rapidly converted to the vinyl complexes at room temperature (Clark and von Werner, 1975). The geometry about the olefinic unit is cis in both cases. Pentacoordinate complexes, in general, appear to be more resistant to insertion (Clark and Manzer, 1974; Clark and Puddephatt, 1971). Here again, conversion of these vinyl complexes to organic products was not studied.

$$(COD)\,[R_2B(pz)_2]PtMe \xrightarrow{R^1-\equiv-R^1} [R_2B(pz)_2]Pt\underset{R^1}{\overset{Me}{\diagdown}}\!\!\!\diagup\!\!\!-R^1 + COD$$

(VIII)

$$(COD)\,[R_2B(pz)_2]Pt\overset{R^1}{\diagup}\!\!=\!\!\underset{Me}{\overset{R^1}{\diagdown}} \longleftarrow$$

(66)

pz = 1, 2-pyrazole
COD = 1, 5-cyclooctadiene

A report of the interaction of $(Ph_3P)_3RhCH_3$ with diphenylacetylene has appeared (Michman and Balog, 1971). In refluxing xylene, a complex mixture of alkylated, isomerized, and oligomerized products was obtained after hydrolysis [Eq. (67)]. It is apparent that much remains to be done before these reactions have any synthetic value.

$$PhC \equiv CPh + (Ph_3P)_3RhCH_3 \xrightarrow[\Delta]{xylene} \xrightarrow{H_2O}$$

$$PhCMe = CHMe + PhCH = CHPh + Ph(PhCH_2)C = CH_2 \tag{67}$$

$$+ \quad PhCH = CPhCPh = CHPh \quad +$$

c. Alkyne Insertions. The interaction of transition metal carbonyls and their derivatives with acetylenes often results in the formation of complex products incorporating more than one alkyne unit and sometimes carbonyl or other ligands. Among the organic products of these reactions are cyclopentadienones, substituted benzenes, quinones, and cyclooctatetraenes (Hübel, 1968; Otsuka and Nakamura, 1976a). A variety of organometallic species is formed as well. Although transient acetylene complexes presumably are intermediates in these reactions, our attention will focus on those for which such complexes are isolable or detectable.

The mechanisms of some of these oligomerization processes have been elucidated through the isolation of intermediates. Three pathways which have been identified are outlined below [Eqs. (68)–(70)]. At present, the

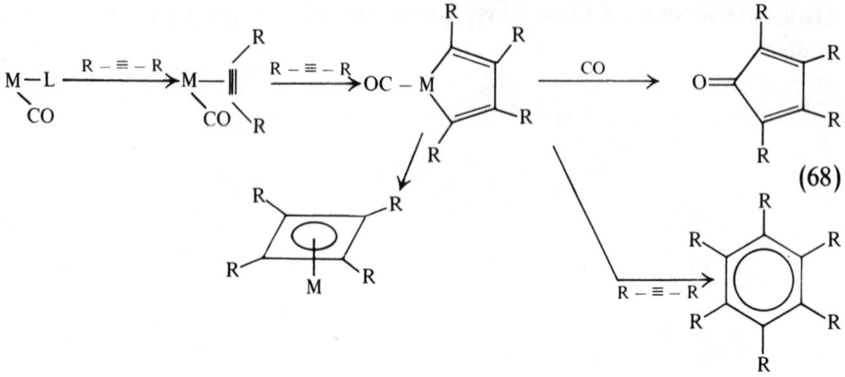

(68)

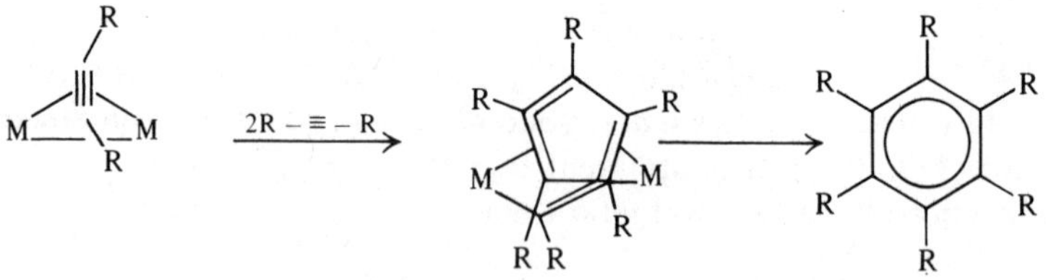

(69)

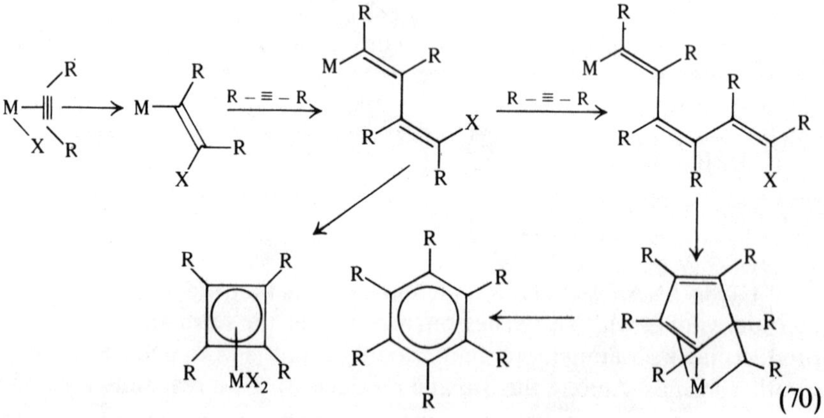

(70)

process involving metallocyclopentadiene intermediates is by far the most common, with the sequences in Eqs. (69) and (70) being confined to dinuclear cobalt complexes (Krüerke and Hübel, 1961) and palladium (II) (Maitlis, 1976) species, respectively. It is convenient to organize further discussion of acetylene insertions according to the number of acetylenes incorporated into the products.

Instances in which cyclobutadiene complexes are the major products from the reactions of acetylene complexes with additional alkyne are uncommon. These generally have been found to be significant products with sterically hindered alkynes and with palladium and platinum metals. For example, phenyl *tert*-butyl acetylene was converted to the corresponding cyclobutadiene complex (one isomer) upon treatment with $(PhCN)_2 PdCl_2$ (Hosokawa and Moritani, 1969) [Eq. (71)]. With sterically less demanding tolane,

$$Ph- \equiv -\!\!\!-\!\!\!\!\!\!\!+ \quad \xrightarrow{(PhCN)_2PdCl_2} \quad \left[\begin{array}{c} Ph \\ \boxed{\bigcirc} -PdCl_2 \\ Ph \end{array} \right]_2 \tag{71}$$

$$Ph- \equiv -Ph \quad \xrightarrow{(PhCN)_2PdCl_2} \quad \left[\begin{array}{c} Ph \quad Ph \\ \boxed{\bigcirc} - PdCl_2 \\ Ph \quad Ph \end{array} \right]_2 + \quad \underset{Ph}{\overset{Ph}{\bigcirc}} \tag{72}$$

hexaphenylbenzene accompanies formation of the cyclobutadiene complex (Malatesta *et al.*, 1960). Maitlis (1976) has proposed a mechanism for the formation of cyclobutadiene complexes in these reactions involving electrocyclization of an intermediate σ-butadienyl complex.

Generation of organic compounds from these cyclobutadiene complexes has not been studied extensively. Treatment of the tetraphenylcyclobutadiene complex with $LiAlH_4$ afforded the corresponding cyclobutene, while its reaction with air in the presence of PPh_3 gave a mixture of the tetrasubstituted furans in unspecified yield (Hosokawa and Moritani, 1969).

$$\left[\begin{array}{c} Ph \quad Ph \\ \boxed{\bigcirc} -PdCl_2 \\ Ph \quad Ph \end{array} \right]_2 \quad \xrightarrow{LiAlH_4} \quad \boxed{} \tag{73}$$

$$\Big\downarrow {\scriptstyle O_2 \atop PPh_3} \tag{74}$$

The reactions of the palladium–cyclobutadiene complexes with excess alkyne produced persubstituted cyclooctatetraenes in analogy to Reppe's catalytic cyclooctatetraene synthesis (Pollock and Maitlis, 1966; Reppe and Schweckendiek, 1948). Although the cyclobutadiene ligand can be transferred between metals [Eq. (76)] (Maitlis, 1971b), liberation of the ligand

$$
\begin{bmatrix} \text{Ar} \quad \text{Ar} \\ \\ \text{Ar} \quad \text{PdX}_2 \quad \text{Ar} \end{bmatrix}_2 \xrightarrow[\substack{\text{PPh}_3 \\ (92\% \text{ Ar} = \text{Ph})}]{\text{Ar} - \equiv - \text{Ar}} \quad \text{[octasubstituted cyclooctatetraene]} \quad + \quad (\text{Ph}_3\text{P})_2\text{PdX}_2 \qquad (75)
$$

from the palladium complexes for synthetic or mechanistic study has not been investigated. Chisholm and Clark (1972) found that the cationic

$$
\begin{bmatrix} \text{Ph} \quad \text{Ph} \\ \\ \text{Ph} \quad \text{PdCl}_2 \quad \text{Ph} \end{bmatrix}_2 \xrightarrow{\text{Fe(CO)}_5} \quad \begin{array}{c} \text{Ph} \quad \text{Ph} \\ \\ \text{Ph} \quad \text{Ph} \\ \text{Fe(CO)}_3 \end{array} \qquad (76)
$$

complex (IX) reacted with excess 2-butyne to give the cyclobutadiene complex, but further transformations of the latter were not reported.

$$
[(\text{Ph}_2\text{MeP})_2(\text{CF}_3)\text{Pt(acetone)}]^+ \xrightarrow[(60\%)]{\text{Me} - \equiv - \text{Me}} \quad \begin{array}{c} \text{Me} \quad \text{Me} \\ \\ \text{Me} \quad \text{Me} \end{array} \overset{+}{\text{Pt}}(\text{CF}_3)(\text{PPh}_2\text{Me}) \qquad (77)
$$
$$
\text{(IX)}
$$

Metallocycles, as noted earlier, frequently are intermediates in the cyclo-oligomerization of acetylenes. In several cases, e.g., Fe (Hoogzand and Hübel, 1968), Ru (Sears and Stone, 1968), Os (Ferraris and Gervasio, 1974), Co (Wakatsuki and Yamazaki, 1973), Rh (Müller et al., 1971), Ir (Collman et al., 1968), Ni (Zeiss and Tsutsui, 1959), and Pd (Ito et al., 1972), these compounds have been isolated and found to undergo several interesting and synthetically important reactions [Eq. (78)]. When unsymmetrical alkynes

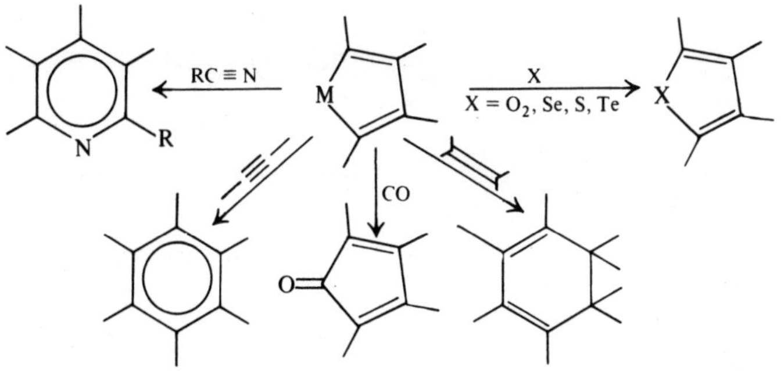

(78)

are coupled to form metallocycles, three isomeric products are possible [A, B, and C in Eq. (79)]. The regioselectivity of insertion is of interest regarding the possible synthesis of specifically substituted cyclic compounds. The reac-

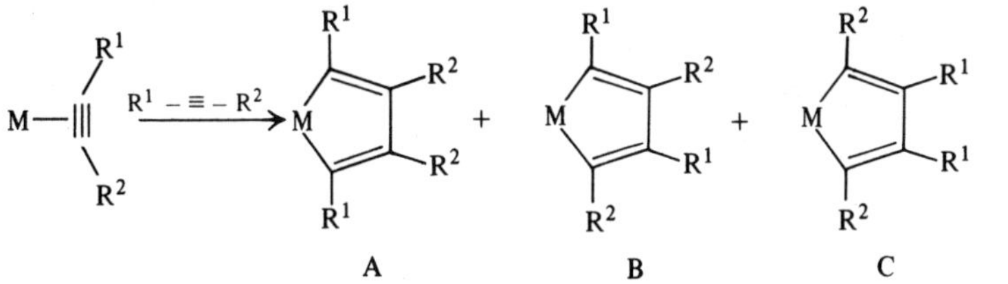

(79)

tions of $CpCo(PPh_3)(R^1C_2R^2)$ with unsymmetrical alkynes, $R^1C_2R^2$ and $R^3C_2R^4$, have been investigated by Wakatsuki and Yamazaki (see Wakat-suki et al., 1974a). Of the three isomers possible when the alkyne is $R^1C_2R^2$, only A and B were formed, the relative amounts depending upon R^1 and R^2.

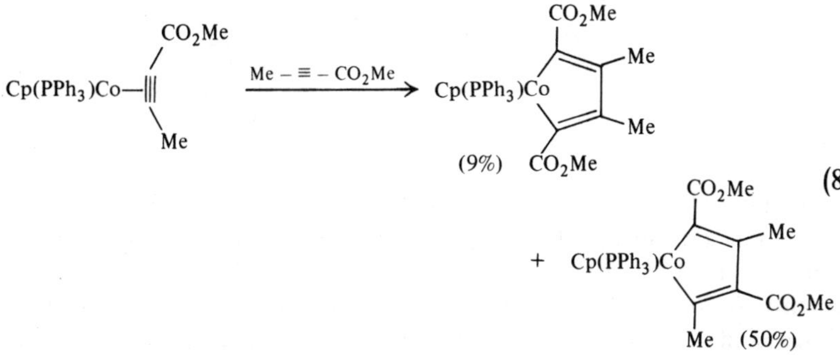

(80)

$$
\text{Cp(PPh}_3\text{)Co}-\underset{\underset{\text{CO}_2\text{Me}}{\diagdown}}{\overset{\overset{\text{Ph}}{\diagup}}{\text{\textbardbl}}} \quad \xrightarrow{\text{Me}-\equiv-\text{CO}_2\text{Me}} \quad \text{Cp(PPh}_3\text{)Co} \quad (81)
$$

(9%) (39%)

In one case examined, in which the alkyne added was different than the one present in the alkyne complex, only two of four possible metallocycles were obtained [Eq. (81)]. Otsuka and Nakamura (1976a) have interpreted the regioselectivity of these and other acetylene insertions in terms of combined steric effects and electronic contributions D, E, and F. Although understand-

$$
\text{M}-\text{\textbardbl} \quad \xrightarrow{\Delta} \quad \overset{+}{\text{M}} \quad \longleftrightarrow \quad \overset{-}{\text{M}} \quad \overset{+}{\text{C}} \quad \longleftrightarrow \quad \dot{\text{M}}
$$

D   E   F

ing of the regioselectivities must be regarded as incomplete at present, the results are promising for synthetic exploitation, especially since the isomers that are obtained can be separated chromatographically.

The great majority of work dealing with conversion of metallocyclopenta-dienes to organic products has involved two classes of compounds, (X) and (XI). We shall begin here by discussing the conversion of these complexes to

Rh(PPh$_3$)$_2$Cl   Co—PPh$_3$

(X)   (XI)

five-membered heterocycles. The rhodacycles, which are formed in good yield upon treatment of bis-α-ketoacetylenes with Wilkinson's catalyst (Müller et al., 1971) [the "diyne reaction," Eq. (82)], react with Group VI elements to afford furans, thiophenes, selenophenes, and tellurophenes (Müller and Winter, 1975; Müller et al., 1975; Müller and Beissner, 1973). Selected examples are presented below. The yields in these reactions are

$$(82)$$

$$(83)$$

$$(84)$$

$$(85)$$

quite variable, with the formation of furans being somewhat less efficient than the formation of the other heterocycles. A process which would permit recycling of the rhodium-containing products from these reactions is needed in order to make them synthetically practical.

The cobalt system (XI) has the attractive feature of allowing preparation of unsymmetrically substituted heterocycles through the stepwise incorporation of two different alkynes [e.g., Eq. (81)]. The cobaltacycles have likewise been treated with sulfur, selenium, and nitrosobenzene to produce the corresponding unsaturated heterocycles as illustrated in Eqs. (86)–(88) (Wakat-

$$(86)$$

$$\text{(87)}$$

$$\text{(88)}$$

suki et al., 1974a). Based on economic considerations, recycling of the cobalt in these cases is considerably less important than for the analogous rhodium reactions.

Cyclotrimerization of acetylenes to form benzene derivatives has probably been the most studied of all organometallic reactions of acetylenes. A few reviews of the subject have appeared (Hübel, 1968; Bowden and Lever, 1968; Otsuka and Nakamura, 1976a; Dickson and Fraser, 1974). The same or different acetylenes can be incorporated to produce several possible substitution patterns. Trimerization of symmetrical alkynes produces hexasubstituted benzenes, while unsymmetrical alkynes may lead to 1,3,5- or 1,2,4-trisubstituted derivatives.

Cobalt complexes, including $Co_2(CO)_8$, $(RC_2R)Co_2(CO)_6$, and (RC_2R)-$Co_4(CO)_{10}$, have been widely employed both stoichiometrically and catalytically for cyclotrimerization (Hübel, 1968). The preparation of completely substituted benzenes by this method is quite general [Eq. (89)] (Krüerke and Hübel, 1961), failing only with extremely bulky acetylenes (e.g., Me_3CC_2-CMe_3, $Me_3SiC_2SiMe_3$) or in cases where the substituents may themselves enter into side reactions with the cobalt atoms (e.g., $R = NO_2$, NH_2). There is no advantage, in fact, in carrying out such trimerizations stoichiometrically from the acetylene complexes; they are most conveniently performed catalytically with cobalt carbonyl itself.

$$(PhC_2Ph)Co_2(CO)_6 \xrightarrow[\substack{\text{toluene, } \Delta \\ (84\%)}]{PhC_2Ph}$$

$$\text{(89)}$$

The trimerization of unsymmetrical alkynes is also effectively catalyzed by $(RC_2R^1)Co_2(CO)_6$. Trimerization of terminal alkynes produces 1,2,4-substituted products specifically [Eq. (90)] (Krüerke and Hübel, 1961). Sym-

$$(RC_2H)Co_2(CO)_6 + RC_2H \xrightarrow{100°} \qquad (90)$$

$$(R = Me_3C, CF_3, Ph, Me_3Si)$$

$$(RC_2R^1)Co_2(CO)_6 + RC_2R^1 \xrightarrow{100°} \qquad (91)$$

$$(R = Ph, R^1 = Me; R = Ph, R^1 = CO_2Me)$$

metrically substituted products are formed, however, with internal alkynes as illustrated in Eq. (91). Here again, there is little to be gained by carrying out these reactions stoichiometrically. Cooligomerization of two different acetylenes, however, is best effected by combining the cobalt complex of one alkyne with a second free alkyne. Ortho-di-*tert*-butylbenzene and 1,2,4,5-tetra-*tert*-butylbenzene have been synthesized by this method [Eqs. (92) and (93)] (Krüerke *et al.*, 1961). These compounds certainly would be difficult to

$$(HC_2H)Co_2(CO)_6 + Me_3CC_2H \xrightarrow{\Delta} (HC_2H)(Me_3CC_2H)Co_2(CO)_4 \qquad (92)$$

$$\downarrow Br_2$$

$$(Me_3CC_2CMe_3)Co_2(CO)_6 + Me_3CC_2H \xrightarrow{\Delta} \xrightarrow{Br_2} \qquad (93)$$

obtain by more conventional means. The so-called "flyover" complexes of composition $(alkyne)_3Co_2(CO)_4$ **(XII)** are intermediates in the cyclotrimerization reactions (Dickson and Fraser, 1974; Krüerke and Hübel, 1961; Mills and Robinson, 1959). These complexes efficiently produce benzenes bearing the same substitution pattern upon heating or treatment with bro-

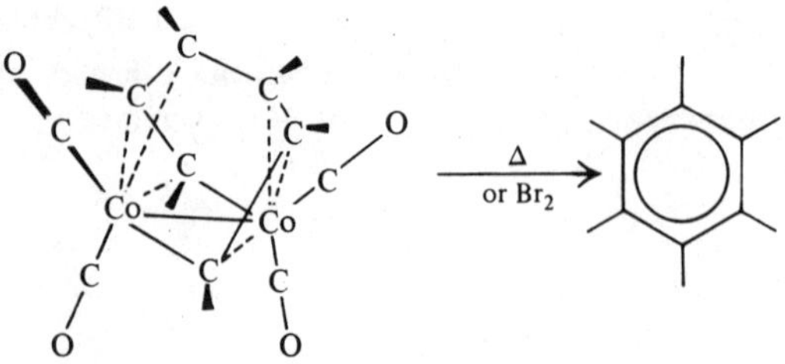

(94)

(XII)

mine. The preferred location of bulky substituents on the terminal carbon of the six-carbon bridge ultimately leads to the hindered aromatic upon ring closure.

Mixed cyclizations of two or three different acetylenes also have been accomplished by the metallocycle route. Stepwise addition of three acetylenes to $CpCo(PPh_3)_2$ has been utilized to produce arenes of diverse substitution patterns as outlined in Eq. (95) (Wakatsuki *et al.*, 1974a). The

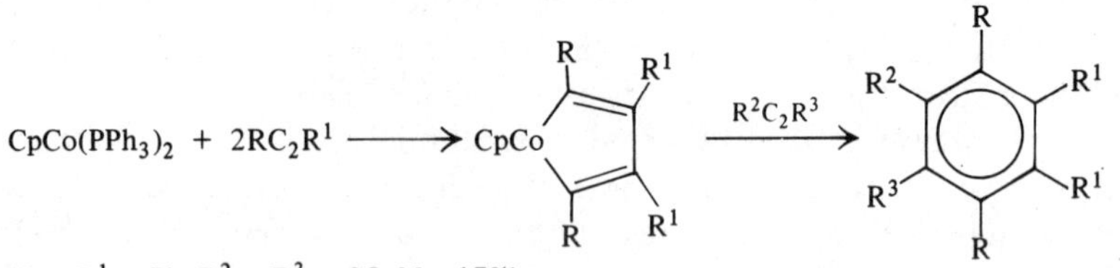

$CpCo(PPh_3)_2 + 2RC_2R^1 \longrightarrow CpCo \xrightarrow{R^2C_2R^3}$

(R = R^1 = Ph, R^2 = R^3 = CO$_2$Me: 17%)
(R = Ph, R^1 = Me, R^2 = Ph, R^3 = CO$_2$Me: 59%)

(95)

regioselectivity observed in metallocycle formation and the possibility of stepwise acetylene addition imparts considerable synthetic value to this method as a route to polysubstituted arenes.

Mixed cyclizations also have been achieved via the "diyne" reaction [Eq. (82)]. Most of the diynes employed thus far have been symmetrical, leading, therefore, to symmetrical rhodacycles. A few representative examples are provided below. An interesting variation is the addition of strained

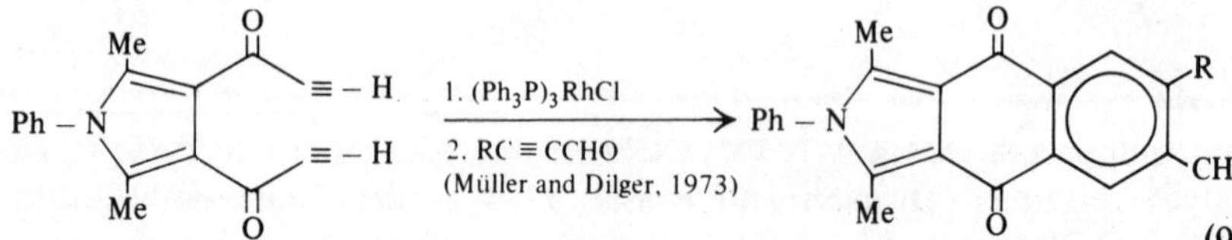

1. (Ph$_3$P)$_3$RhCl
2. RC ≡ CCHO
(Müller and Dilger, 1973)

(96)

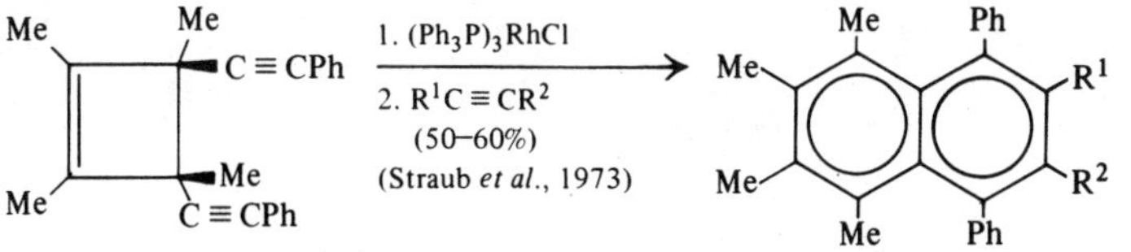

(97)

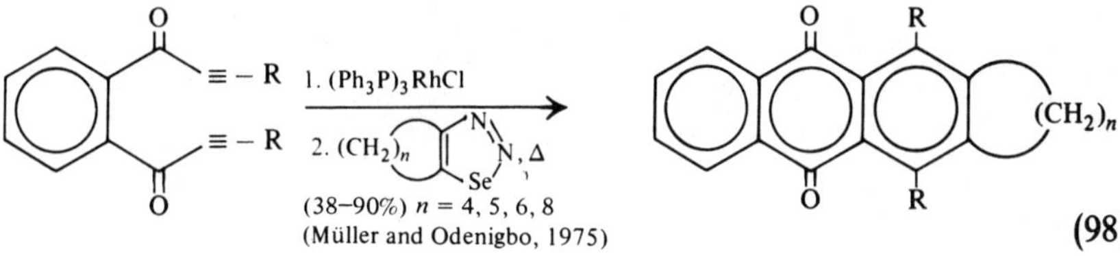

(98)

cycloalkynes and benzyne to the intermediate metallocyclopentadienes as illustrated in Eq. (98).

A synthetically important catalytic mixed cyclotrimerization has been developed recently by Vollhardt using $CpCo(CO)_2$ (Vollhardt, 1977). By combining diynes with bis(trimethylsilyl)acetylene, an alkyne incapable of self-condensation, bicyclic aromatics, including tetralins, indanes, and benzocyclobutenes, are readily obtained (Hillard and Vollhardt, 1975). Anthraquinones have also been prepared from diketodiynes (Hillard and Vollhardt,

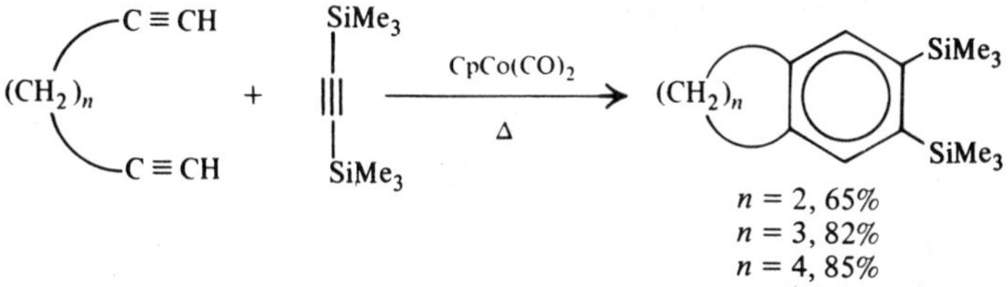

$$n = 2, 65\%$$
$$n = 3, 82\%$$
$$n = 4, 85\%$$

(99)

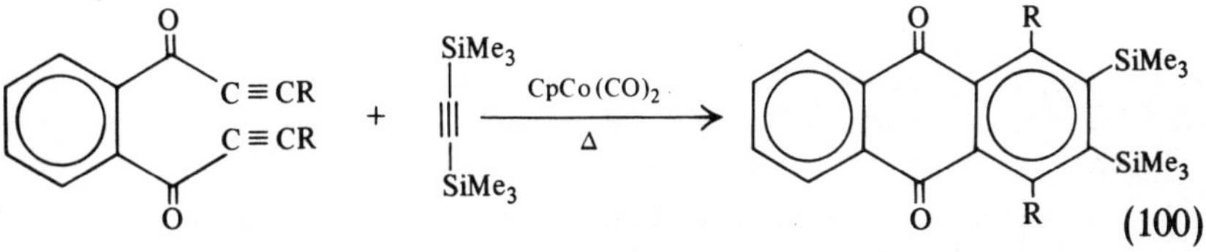

(100)

1977). Using 1,5-diynes as precursors to *o*-xylylenes, which then are trapped by $Me_3SiC_2SiMe_3$, or trapped intramolecularly by using diynes substituted with side chains bearing potential dienophiles, polycyclic systems are generated in a one-pot reaction from acyclic starting materials (Funk and Vollhardt, 1976).

$$(101)$$

$$(102)$$

d. Alkene Insertions. The reactions of olefins with alkyne complexes have received relatively little attention. These yield products, including dienes, cyclopentanones, and cyclohexadienes, in which one or more olefin units are coupled to the originally coordinated alkyne.

Pauson and co-workers have investigated the interaction of (alkyne)Co_2-$(CO)_6$ species with various olefins. The strained substrates norbornene, norbornadiene, and 1,2-dicarbomethoxynorbornadiene afford *exo*-cyclopentenone derivatives in low to moderate yield when heated with cobalt–acetylene complexes (Pauson *et al.*, 1973) [Eq. (103)]. $CpCo(CO)_2$

$$(103)$$

also was obtained, apparently by formal retro-Diels–Alder reaction of the bicyclic starting materials. With unsymmetrical acetylenes (e.g., $R^1 = H$, $R^2 = Me$; $R^1 = H$, $R^2 = Ph$), the larger substituent was located adjacent to the carbonyl group. With norbornenes monosubstituted at the double bond, the substituent carbon was located adjacent to the carbonyl group in the resulting cyclopentenone (Khand and Pauson, 1976). The unsubstituted derivative (R^1, $R^2 = H$) could be prepared catalytically by combining acetylene, norbornadiene, CO, and $Co_2(CO)_8$. Similar reactions with simple, unstrained olefins (Khand and Pauson, 1977a,b) and with cyclobutenes (Bladen *et al.*, 1977a,b) also produce cyclopentenones, but more drastic conditions are required in the former case.

In contrast, when $(PhC_2H)Co_2(CO)_6$ was heated with α,β-unsaturated carbonyl compounds, conjugated dienes were obtained in moderate yield [Eq. (104)] (Khand and Pauson, 1974). Crotonaldehyde gave the corre-

$$(PhC_2H)Co_2(CO)_6 \ + \ CH_3CH = CHCO_2Et \ \xrightarrow[\quad(45\%)\quad]{\Delta} \ PhCH = CH - C\,(CH_3) = CHCO_2Et$$
$$(t,t \,/c,t \, \sim 3.5/1)$$

$$(104)$$

sponding trans, trans aldehyde. The applicability of this reaction to complexes of other alkynes was not investigated, nor was its mechanism discussed.

Coupling of olefins and acetylenes also has been accomplished using (alkyne)CpCo(PPh$_3$). Cyclohexadienes, linear hexadienes, or trienes have been obtained, depending on the olefin employed. For example, the complex (XIII) reacted with dimethyl maleate to product a single isolable metallocyclopentene complex (Wakatsuki et al., 1974b). This, in turn, reacted with additional alkyne to afford a cyclohexadiene complex. Similar products also

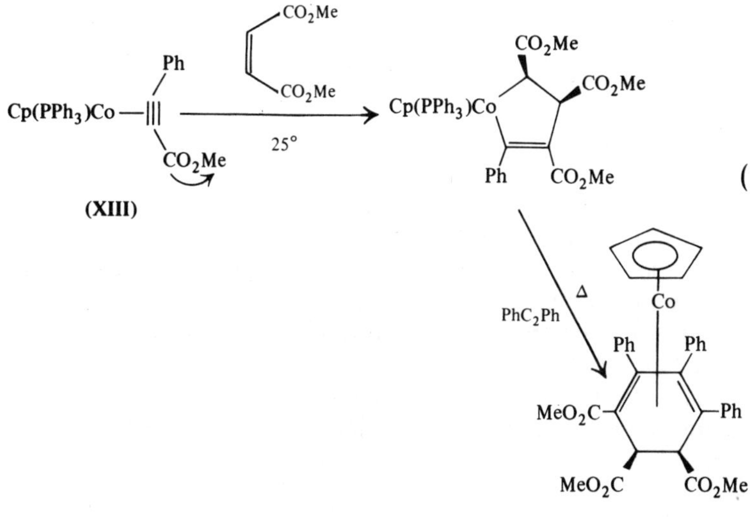

$$(105)$$

were obtained by reversing the order of the above reactions. The metallocycle, prepared from the tolane complex and methyl propiolate, reacted with dimethyl maleate, giving the corresponding diene complex (Wakatsuki et al., 1974a). The dienes were liberated upon treatment of the complexes with ceric salts. In some cases, the free dienes were produced directly upon treatment of the metallocycle with olefin. When the acetylene complexes were

$$(106)$$

employed as catalysts in combination with unsaturated nitriles and alkynes, linear products were obtained [Eq. (102)] by an undetermined mechanism (Wakatsuki *et al.*, 1974b).

$$(107)$$

e. Carbon Monoxide Insertions. Insertion of carbon monoxide into the metal–acetylene bond is often one step in a multistep process leading to complex products incorporating one or more carbonyls and one or more alkyne units. Among the organic products isolated from such reactions are esters, lactones, cyclopentadienones, and quinones.

Products which arise from combination of one CO molecule and one alkyne molecule are relatively uncommon. Treatment of $(HC_2H)Co_2(CO)_6$

$$(HC_2H)Co_2(CO)_6 \xrightarrow[\text{EtOH}]{\text{CO}} CH_2 = CHCO_2Et + CH_3CH_2CO_2Et$$

$$(35-60\%) \qquad\qquad (2-15\%)$$

$$+ \; \begin{array}{c} CH_2CO_2Et \\ | \\ CH_2CO_2Et \end{array}$$

$$(29-49\%)$$

$$(108)$$

with CO in ethanol solution produces a mixture of ethyl acrylate, ethyl propionate, and diethyl succinate (Iwashita *et al.*, 1973). The product distribution was dependent on the reaction conditions. Extension of the reaction to substituted acetylenes has not been reported. Whereas ceric oxidation of dicobalt hexacarbonyl complexes of internal acetylenes liberates the acetylene, Pauson has reported that oxidation of the corresponding phenylacetylene complex in ethanol gives the one-carbon homologated ester [Eq. (109)] (Khand *et al.*, 1974). It is not known whether this reaction is applicable to other terminal acetylenes.

$$(PhC_2H)Co_2(CO)_6 \xrightarrow[\substack{EtOH \\ (40\%)}]{(NH_4)_2Ce(NO_3)_6} PhC \equiv C - CO_2Et \tag{109}$$

In the absence of nucleophilic solvents, $(RC_2H)Co_2(CO)_6$ compounds are carbonylated to produce butenolide complexes (**XIV**) in variable yields (Sternberg *et al.*, 1959; Sauer *et al.*, 1959; Mills and Robinson, 1967; Guthrie *et al.*, 1975; Pályi *et al.*, 1975). Complexes of internal alkynes generally fail to

$$(RC_2H)Co_2(CO)_6 \xrightarrow[\substack{70° \\ (30-90\%)}]{CO\ (200\ atm)} \tag{110}$$

(XIV)

react, presumably for steric reasons. The reaction for terminal alkynes is regioselective, as shown, giving the 2-substituted lactone derivatives. These complexes react further with CO to afford novel, dimeric lactones (bifurandiones) (**XV**) in which the unsymmetrical dimer predominates. It is interesting that for R = H, however, only the symmetrical product was formed when tetramethyl urea was used as solvent (Sauer *et al.*, 1959). The bifurandiones also can be produced catalytically from alkynes, CO, and $Co_2(CO)_8$ (Sauer *et al.*, 1959). A few other reactions of the butenolide complexes have been briefly examined. Treatment of **XIV** (R = Ph) with $NaBH_4$ afforded the monomeric, unsaturated lactone, while oxidation gave maleic esters (Guthrie *et al.*, 1975).

$$(111)$$

R = H, Ph

Although cyclopentadienones and quinones often are produced in the reactions of metal carbonyls with acetylenes, they are seldom the major products, hence these reactions are of little practical synthetic value. Although not extensively investigated, a route of possible generality involves treatment of metallocyclopentadienes with carbon monoxide. The cobaltacycle (XVI) thus was converted to the tetraphenylcyclopentadienone com-

$$(112)$$

plex when heated with CO (Yamazaki and Hagihara, 1967). Effective methods for regenerating the dienones do not appear to have been developed.

Nesmeyanov and co-workers (1971) have found that thermolysis of tolane complex (XVII) gives diphenylindenone as the major product. Formation of this product was suggested to occur through a complexed benzyne intermediate. Attempted preparation of the corresponding lead complex gave only the indenone derivative in 58% yield.

$$(113)$$

f. Miscellaneous Insertions. Mixed cyclization of acetylenes with nitriles provides a convenient route to pyridine derivatives according to Eq. (114).

$$2RC_2R + RCN \xrightarrow{M} \qquad (114)$$

The cobaltacycles derived from the reaction of alkynes with $CpCo(PPh_3)_2$ yield substituted pyridines upon treatment with nitriles (Wakatsuki *et al.*,

$$Cp(PPh_3)Co \xrightarrow[\substack{70° \\ (30-70\%)}]{R'CN} \qquad (115)$$

$(R = Ph, CO_2Me)$

1974a). Regioselective formation of particular isomers by this route can be anticipated in light of the selectivity noted previously for formation of the metallocycles. In some cases, these reactions can be carried out catalytically (Wakatsuki *et al.*, 1974a; Bonnemann *et al.*, 1974), albeit in somewhat depressed yield, presumably as a result of self-trimerization of the alkyne. Incorporation of two different alkynes also would be impractical by this procedure. Also of interest is the cyclooligomerization of α,ω-diynes with nitriles with $CpCo(CO)_2$ as catalyst. Using this reaction, tetrahydroquinolines can be prepared in good yield [Eq. (116)] (Vollhardt, 1977).

$$(116)$$

The interaction of isocyanides with acetylene complexes has been found to produce various organic and organometallic products differing in the number of alkyne and isocyanide units incorporated. $Cp(Ph_3P)Co(PhC_2Ph)$ reacts with two equivalents of isocyanide to form the diimino cobaltacycle (**XVIII**) (Yamazaki *et al.*, 1975). Further reaction of these complexes with additional isocyanide led to the novel cyclopentene derivatives (**XIX**). These

$$Cp(PPh_3)Co(PhC_2Ph) \ + \ 2RNC \ \xrightarrow{\ \ 25° \ \ }$$

(117)

(XVIII)

(XIX)

latter compounds also were produced catalytically, for example, by cocyclization of tolane and 2,6-dimethylphenyl isocyanide.

In contrast to the above results, the nickel isocyanide complexes react with tolane to afford diiminocyclobutenes in variable yield (Suzuki and Takizawa, 1972). These reactions presumably proceed via mixed isocyanide–acetylene complexes since these can be prepared independently and gave the same product on thermolysis. The imino compounds are readily hydrolyzed to cyclobutenediones.

$$(RNC)_4Ni \ + \ PhC_2Ph \ \xrightarrow[(22-90\%)]{\ \ 130° \ \ } \ [(RNC)_2Ni(PhC_2Ph)]$$

(118)

In a final variation, the hexafluorobutyne–molybdenum and –tungsten complexes (**XX**) and (**XXI**) react with excess *tert*-butyl isocyanide to afford iminocyclopentadiene complexes (Davidson *et al.*, 1975). Release of the diene ligand from this complex was not reported.

Scattered reports have appeared involving insertions of other molecules into metal–acetylene complexes. The most noteworthy examples from a synthetic perspective deal with the reactions of CS_2 and OCS with cyclopen-

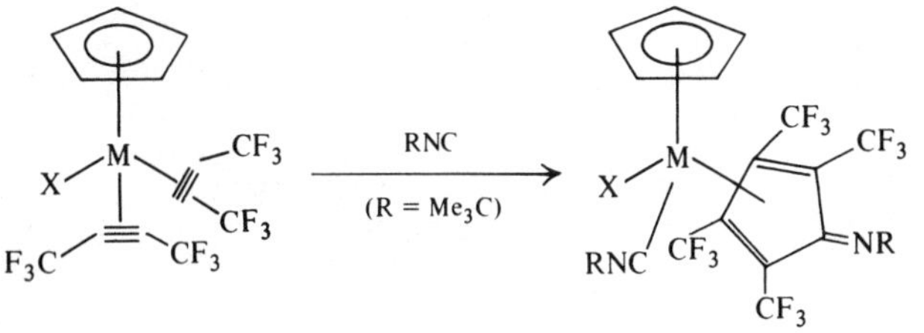

(119)

(XX)   (M = Mo, X = CF$_3$)
(XXI)   (M = W, X = Cl)

tadienyl cobalt and rhodium complexes (Wakatsuki et al., 1973). Complexes of both metals react with CS$_2$ to produce metallothiolactone derivatives. These were quantitatively converted to heterocycles upon treatment with elemental sulfur or to thiolactone derivatives with cyclohexyl isocyanide.

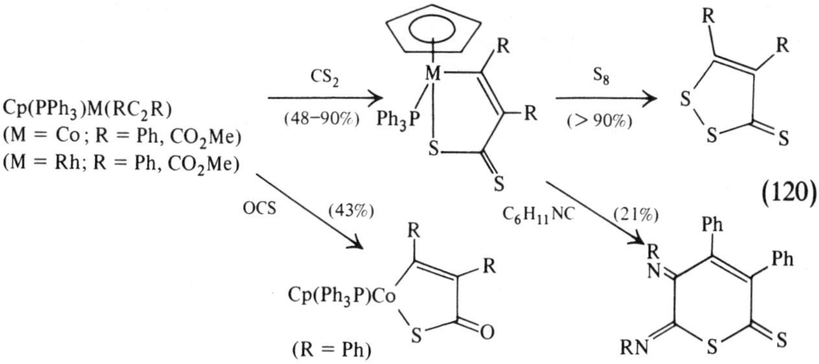

Cp(PPh$_3$)M(RC$_2$R)
(M = Co; R = Ph, CO$_2$Me)
(M = Rh; R = Ph, CO$_2$Me)

(120)

(XXII)

The reaction with OCS gave the metallocycle (XXII) as the only isomer which was not converted to organic products.

V. SYNTHESIS AND REACTIONS OF ALKYLIDYNETRICOBALT NONACARBONYL COMPLEXES

While cluster complexes which contain a CM$_3$ tetrahedral core also are known for M = Ni (Voyevodskaya et al., 1972), Ru (Deeming and Underhill, 1973, 1974; Canty et al., 1972), and Os (Deeming et al., 1974), only the synthesis and chemistry of the cobalt clusters of type RCCo$_3$(CO)$_9$, which contains the tetrahedral CCo$_3$ core (Fig. 2), have been examined in detail. A wide variety of such complexes has been prepared and the organic chemistry of this novel class of organometallic complexes is well developed. Reviews

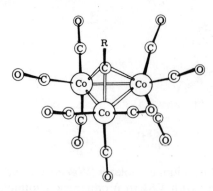

Fig. 2 Structure of an alkylidynetricobalt nonacarbonyl complex.

concerning $RCCo_3(CO)_9$ complexes are available (Seyferth, 1976; Pályi *et al.*, 1970; Penfold and Robinson, 1973), and a volume of the Gmelin Handbook of Inorganic Chemistry New Supplement Series deals with them in detail (Gmelin, 1973).

A. Preparation

As noted in Section III,B,1, one general route to $RCCo_3(CO)_9$ complexes uses dicobalt hexacarbonyl complexes of terminal acetylenes, $(RC_2H)Co_2(CO)_6$, as starting materials. When these are treated with acids such as sulfuric acid in refluxing methanol (Markby *et al.*, 1958; Robinson and Spencer, 1971; Tominaga *et al.*, 1970), the conversion to $RCH_2CCo_3(CO)_9$ complexes takes place, with the acetylenic carbon atom which carried the hydrogen substituent being incorporated into the CCo_3 core. The mechanism of this $(RC_2H)Co_2(CO)_6 \rightarrow RCH_2CCo_3(CO)_9$ conversion is unknown. Examples of such reactions are known for $R = H$, CH_3, CF_3, CH_3O_2C, C_2H_5, $HO(CH_2)_3$, $n\text{-}C_3H_7$, $(CH_3)_2CH$, Ph_2CH, Me_3C, Ph, $p\text{-}BrC_6H_4$, and C_6F_5 (Dickson and Fraser, 1974). In some cases, $RCH_2CCo_3(CO)_9$ complexes are formed simply by heating the terminal alkyne with dicobalt octacarbonyl or with $Co_4(CO)_{12}$ (Dickson and Fraser, 1974).

A more generally applicable reaction is that of organic trihalides with dicobalt octacarbonyl or with a salt of the $Co(CO)_4^-$ anion, reactions which may be carried out in donor solvents such as tetrahydrofuran or in hydrocarbon solvents such as benzene (Dent *et al.*, 1961; Ercoli *et al.*, 1962; Bor *et al.*, 1961, 1962; Seyferth *et al.*, 1973a). A wide variety of R groups [Eq. (121)]

$$RCX_3 + Co_2(CO)_8 \longrightarrow RCCo_3(CO)_9 + CoX_2 + CO + \cdots \qquad (121)$$

may be accommodated in this synthesis: H, halogen, alkyl, aryl, vinyl, and functional groups such as CO_2R', $C(O)R'$, $C(O)NMe_2$, $R_3'Si$, $(R'O)_2P(O)$, but in some cases (R = CH$_2$OH, CHO) the expected products are not obtained at all or in only trace yield. A few dihalides—PhCHCl$_2$, MeOCHCl$_2$, [Me$_2$N=CHCl]Cl—will react with dicobalt octacarbonyl to give RCCo$_3$-(CO)$_9$ products (Seyferth *et al.*, 1973a). The yields in these reactions are variable, with the range of 25–50% being typical. Here again, the mechanism of these reactions which give RCCo$_3$(CO)$_9$ clusters has not been elucidated.

B. Interconversions of Alkylidynetricobalt Nonacarbonyl Complexes

Before we discuss the interconversion reactions by which one cluster complex, RCCo$_3$(CO)$_9$, may be transformed into another, R'CCo$_3$(CO)$_9$, it is useful to mention, if only briefly, something about the physical properties of RCCo$_3$(CO)$_9$ compounds. Most of them are crystalline solids which are deeply colored—from red through purple through brown through black. Most are stable to air, as the solid or in solution. Most are thermally stable and can be handled at room temperature, although some do decompose on prolonged storage at room temperature. Many are sufficiently stable thermally to permit their purification by recrystallization from hot solvents or by sublimation at 50°–60° in high vacuum. They are soluble in the common organic solvents, so column chromatography and thin-layer chromatography may be used with advantage to resolve mixtures of RCCo$_3$-(CO)$_9$ complexes. Their characteristic absorptions in the terminal carbonyl region, ca. 2100–1975 cm^{-1}, makes infrared spectroscopy useful in their identification. The RCCo$_3$(CO)$_9$ complexes are diamagnetic, so nmr spectra of these compounds present no unusual features. While they are, in general, stable toward protic and Lewis acids, strong bases (OH$^-$, OR$^-$, RLi, etc.) and various nucleophiles will destroy them. Oxidizing agents stronger than molecular oxygen convert them to oxidized organic products and inorganic cobalt compounds. Such processes will be discussed in more detail later in this section.

The interconversions of such methylidynetricobalt nonacarbonyl complexes obtained by the direct, Co$_2$(CO)$_8$-based routes, particularly, HCCo-(CO)$_9$ [prepared by reaction of bromoform with Co$_2$(CO)$_8$] and XCCo$_3$-(CO)$_9$ (X = Cl, Br, I), provide a second route to many RCCo$_3$(CO)$_9$ compounds where R can be an alkyl, an aryl, a vinyl, an organofunctional, or a silyl group. The following equations illustrate the types of such reactions which have been reported.

HCCo$_3$(CO)$_9$

$$\text{Ar}_2\text{Hg} + \text{HCCo}_3(\text{CO})_9 \xrightarrow[\text{under CO \quad (65-95\%)}]{\text{C}_6\text{H}_6, \ 80°} \text{ArCCo}_3(\text{CO})_9 + \text{ArH} + \text{Hg} \qquad (122)$$

This reaction also can be effected with arylmercuric halides and, much less well, with dialkylmercurials and alkylmercuric halides. Excellent yields generally are obtained, except when the Ar group is a highly hindered one such as mesityl or pentachlorophenyl (Seyferth et al., 1974a).

$$Z_3SiH + HCCo_3(CO)_9 \xrightarrow[\text{under CO} \ (75-90\%)]{C_6H_5CH_3, \ 105°} Z_3SiCCo_3(CO)_9 + H_2 \qquad (123)$$

The Z substituent on silicon may be alkyl, aryl, alkoxy, halogen, in any combination (Seyferth and Nivert, 1977a). Product yields are excellent.

$$RCH{=}CH_2 + HCCo_3(CO)_9 \xrightarrow[(10-45\%)]{} RCH_2CH_2CCo_3(CO)_9 \qquad (124)$$

This appears to be a free radical process since it is catalyzed by azobisisobutyronitrile (Seyferth and Hallgren, 1973; Sakamoto et al., 1973; Kamijo et al., 1973). The yields of product generally are low.

$ClCCo_3(CO)_9$ and $BrCCo_3(CO)_9$

$$ArH + XCCo_3(CO)_9 \xrightarrow[(CH_2Cl_2) \ (75-90\%)]{AlX_3} ArCCo_3(CO)_9 + HX \qquad (125)$$

With monosubstituted benzenes, para substitution generally is observed, but when the steric factor associated with the substituent on the benzene nucleus is small, ortho substitution can take place (Dolby and Robinson, 1972). The product yields generally are good.

$$ArMgX + BrCCo_3(CO)_9 \xrightarrow[(25-70\%)]{} ArCCo_3(CO)_9 + MgXBr \qquad (126)$$

A nine-fold excess of the aryl Grignard reagent is required in order to achieve reasonable product yields. Such reactions are not observed with alkyl Grignard reagents or with organolithium reagents (Dolby and Robinson, 1973).

$$XCCo_3(CO)_9 \xrightarrow{AlX_3} [(OC)_9Co_3CCO]^+$$

$$[(OC)_9Co_3CCO]^+ + Nu - H \xrightarrow{} (OC)_9Co_3CC(O)Nu + H^+ \qquad (127)$$
$$\text{(a nucleophile)} \qquad\qquad (50-80\%)$$

When X = Cl and the reaction is carried out in dichloromethane, the acylium ion reagent remains in solution. When X = Br and the reaction is carried out in carbon disulfide, the acylium ion reagent precipitates rapidly as $[(OC)_9Co_3CCO]^+[AlBr_4 \cdot AlBr_3]^-$ (Seyferth *et al.*, 1977a). These charged species react with diverse nucleophiles as shown in Eq. (127): with alcohols and phenols to give esters, $(OC)_9 Co_3 CCO_2R$; with thiols to give thioesters, $(OC)_9 Co_3 CC(O)SR$; with ammonia and amines to give amides, $(OC)_9 Co_3 CC(O)NRR'$; with a few amides to give imides, $(OC)_9Co_3-CC(O)NHC(O)R$; with ethylzinc halide to give

$$(OC)_9Co_3CC(O)Et;$$

with tetramethyltin to give, in a very slow reaction, $(OC)_9 Co_3 CC(O)CH_3$; and with triethylsilane to give the formyl derivative, $(OC)_9 Co_3 CCHO$. Friedel-Crafts acylation of the most reactive aromatic substrates, *N,N*-dimethylaniline, pyrrole, indole, and ferrocene, can be effected with these acylium ion reagents, but on the whole they are relatively unreactive as carbon electrophiles, compared to wholly organic RCO^+ species. The $XCCo_3 (CO)_9$ to $(OC)_9 Co_3 CCO^+$ conversion is an intriguing one which necessarily involves a migration of CO from cobalt to the apical carbon atom, but its mechanism is not yet fully understood.

The aluminum halide in this reaction serves to accelerate a process which in many cases occurs spontaneously when $BrCCo_3 (CO)_9$ is dissolved in the nucleophile, slowly at room temperature, more rapidly at 60° (Ercoli *et al.*, 1962; Ercoli, 1962; Seyferth and Nivert, 1976), e.g.:

$$BrCCo_3(CO)_9 \xrightarrow[\text{under CO} \quad (86\%)]{\text{MeOH, reflux}} (OC)_9Co_3CCO_2Me + HBr \qquad (128)$$

$$BrCCo_3(CO)_9 \xrightarrow[\text{room temperature} \quad (79\%)]{\text{Et}_2\text{NH; rapid at}} (OC)_9Co_3CC(O)NEt_2 + HBr \qquad (129)$$

Triethylamine is effective in inducing such reactions (Seyferth and Nivert, 1976):

$$BrCCo_3(CO)_9 \xrightarrow[\text{24 hr} \quad (46\%)]{\text{MeOH, 25°}} (OC)_9Co_3CCO_2Me \qquad (130)$$

but

$$BrCCo_3(CO)_9 \xrightarrow[\substack{\text{Et}_3\text{N} \quad (80\%) \\ \text{5 hr}}]{\text{MeOH, 25°}} (OC)_9Co_3CCO_2Me \qquad (131)$$

The $BrCCo_3(CO)_9/Et_3N$ combination is effective in the acylation of diverse alcohols and phenols, aniline and its derivatives, and it will even effect acylation of pyrrole and indole. These remarkable reactions also can be effected, but in poorer yield, when $HCCo_3(CO)_9$ is used in place of $BrCCo_3(CO)_9$ (Seyferth and Nivert, 1976).

Functional Group Interconversions

Once an organic functional group has been introduced into the alkylidynetricobalt nonacarbonyl system, it is, within limits, capable of further elaboration. Thus, the ester function in $(OC)_9Co_3CCO_2R$ complexes is readily converted to the acylium ion by the action of strong acid (Seyferth *et al.*, 1974e):

$$(OC)_9Co_3CCO_2R \xrightarrow[\text{(EtCO)}_2O]{\text{HPF}_6} [(OC)_9Co_3CCO]^+PF_6^- \qquad (132)$$

The cluster acylium hexafluorophosphate precipitates from solution and then may be brought into reaction with nucleophiles as shown in Scheme 1. The product yields are in the 60–95% range.

The chemistry of acylmethylidynetricobalt nonacarbonyl compounds has received attention, especially their reduction to the corresponding alcohols. This conversion may be accomplished in good yield by a hydrosilylation/silyl ether solvolysis sequence (Seyferth *et al.*, 1974b):

$$(OC)_9Co_3CC(O)R \xrightarrow[65°]{\text{Et}_3\text{SiH, THF}} (OC)_9Co_3\text{—CCHR}$$

(R = H, alkyl, aryl)

$$\underset{OSiEt_3}{|}$$

$$\downarrow \begin{array}{l} \text{1. conc } H_2SO_4 \\ \text{2. } H_2O \end{array}$$

$$(OC)_9Co_3CH(OH)R \quad (75–85\%)$$

$$(133)$$

When the R in $RC(O)CCo_3(CO)_9$ is an aryl group, then the reduction to the secondary alcohol can be effected in good yield with molecular hydrogen at atmospheric pressure at 80° in the presence of CO and in the absence of an added catalyst (Seyferth *et al.*, 1976). Such reduction by molecular hydrogen occurs also with acyl derivatives (R = alkyl), but the alcohol yields are not high and some completely reduced product, $RCH_2CCo_3(CO)_9$, is formed as well, e.g.:

$$(OC)_9Co_3CC(O)CH_3 \xrightarrow[80°]{\text{H}_2/\text{CO}} (OC)_9Co_3CCH(OH)CH_3 \qquad (31\%)$$

$$+$$

$$(OC)_9Co_3CCH_2CH_3 \qquad (8\%) \qquad (134)$$

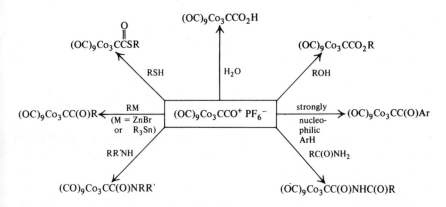

Scheme 1 A general survey of the reactions of $(OC)_9Co_3CCO^+ PF_6^-$.

Another general reaction of the $RC(O)CCo_3(CO)_9$ complexes is their facile decarbonylation, which can be effected simply by heating them under nitrogen in benzene solution at 80°:

$$RC(O)CCo_3(CO)_9 \xrightarrow{\;80°\;} RCCo_3(CO)_9 + CO \qquad (135)$$

This reaction occurs more or less well with almost all $RC(O)CCo_3 (CO)_9$ compounds examined (Seyferth et al., 1973b). For instance, when R = p-$CH_3C_6H_4$, a 69% yield of $p\text{-}CH_3C_6H_4CCo_3 (CO)_9$ was obtained within a reaction time of 6 hr. The mechanisms of the reactions under discussion remain to be studied, but it is clear that they do not involve "standard" organic mechanisms, and it is very likely that the cobalt atoms of the cluster are intimately involved in this novel chemistry.

The availability of alcohols of type $RCH(OH)CCo_3(CO)_9$ (R = H, alkyl, aryl) led to the development of the derived carbonium ions, $[RCHCCo_3\text{-}(CO)_9]^+$, as a class of highly stabilized and relatively unreactive cationic species (Seyferth et al., 1976). The preparative route is shown in the equation below:

$$RCH(OH)CCo_3(CO)_9 \xrightarrow[\text{(EtCO)}_2O]{HPF_6} [RCHCCo_3(CO)_9]^+ PF_6^- \qquad (136)$$

These salts were found to be carbon electrophiles but were relatively unreactive and very selective. They alkylate alcohols and primary amines, e.g.:

$$[CH_2CCo_3(CO)_9]^+ \begin{cases} \xrightarrow[\text{(76\%)}]{\text{EtOH}} EtOCH_2CCo_3(CO)_9 \\[2em] \xrightarrow[\text{(67\%)}]{\text{PhNH}_2} PhNHCH_2CCo_3(CO)_9 \end{cases} \qquad (137)$$

However, they alkylate only the most reactive aromatic nucleophiles such as N,N-dimethylaniline. How cations of the type $[RCHCCo_3 (CO)_9]^+$ are stabilized is not fully understood as yet, but ^{13}C nmr studies suggest that the positive charge resides mainly on the cobalt atoms and that the carbon atom at which the positive charge originally was generated by heterolytic cleavage of OH^- from the alcohol is nearly electroneutral (Seyferth et al., 1974c, 1975a). In any case, the reactions of these cations with nucleophiles provide another route to α-functional derivatives of the $CCo_3(CO)_9$ cluster.

The strong stabilization of a positive charge α to the $CCo_3(CO)_9$ cluster leads to high reactivity of $C_6H_5 CCo_3 (CO)_9$ in Friedel-Crafts acylation (Seyferth et al., 1975b):

$$\text{C}_6\text{H}_5{-}CCo_3(CO)_9 \xrightarrow[\text{CH}_2\text{Cl}_2 \text{ (93\%)}]{\text{CH}_3\text{C(O)Cl, AlCl}_3} CH_3C(O){-}\text{C}_6\text{H}_4{-}CCo_3(CO)_9$$

$$(138)$$

Detailed studies of such reactions were made, and it is of particular interest that a competition study showed $PhCCo_3 (CO)_9$ to be equal in reactivity to N,N-dimethylaniline. Another consequence of the strong stabilization of an α positive charge by the $CCo_3(CO)_9$ cluster is that charged electrophiles add readily to a vinyl-substituted cluster complex in a predictable manner (Seyferth et al., 1974d, 1977b). For instance, oxymercuration of $CH_2 = CHCCo_3 (CO)_9$ using mercuric trifluoroacetate in methanol occurs to give, after treatment of the product with aqueous NaCl, $ClHgCH_2CH(OMe)CCo_3(CO)_9$.

C. Conversion of Alkylidynetricobalt Nonacarbonyl Complexes to Wholly Organic Compounds

The $RCCo_3(CO)_9$ compounds may be regarded as carbyne complexes, in which the $R\dot{C}$: species functions as a triply-bridging ligand which is bonded to the triangulo-nonacarbonyltricobalt unit (Seyferth et al., 1971). This view finds some support in the observed apical carbon atom ^{13}C nmr shieldings:

ca. 275–310 ppm downfield from tetramethylsilane (Seyferth *et al.*, 1975a; Aimé *et al.*, 1976), in the region in which are found the carbyne carbon atom ^{13}C nmr resonances of transition metal–carbyne complexes containing a monodentate $R\dot{C}$: ligand, e.g., $CH_3 C{\equiv}W(CO)_4 Cl$, $\delta_C = 288.8$ ppm (Fischer *et al.*, 1973). The thermal decomposition of such monodentate carbyne complexes results in the formation of an acetylene, i.e., the formal carbyne "dimer" (Fischer, 1976):

$$PhC{\equiv}Cr(CO)_4Br \xrightarrow{\text{30°}} PhC{\equiv}CPh + \cdots \qquad (139)$$

Moreover, the decomposition of $CH_3C{\equiv}Cr(CO)_4Br$ in the presence of dicobalt octacarbonyl resulted in interception of $CH_3 \dot{C}$: to give $CH_3 CCo_3$-$(CO)_9$ (Fischer and Däweritz, 1975). In this context, it is then not surprising that the decomposition of $RCCo_3 (CO)_9$ compounds gives either acetylenes or acetylenedicobalt hexacarbonyl complexes:

$$PhCCo_3(CO)_9 \xrightarrow[\text{(Khand et al., 1974)}]{\text{diglyme, reflux}} Co \text{ metal} + PhC{\equiv}CPh \qquad (140)$$

$$ArCCo_3(CO)_9 \xrightarrow[\text{(Seyferth et al., 1971)}]{\text{MeOH, reflux}} (ArC_2Ar)Co_2(CO)_6 \qquad (141)$$

$$[Ar = Ph, p\text{-}CH_3C(O)C_6H_4]$$

These processes are inefficient and the product yields are low. It has been reported that acetylenes also are formed, among other organic products, when alkylidynetricobalt nonacarbonyl complexes are oxidized using a limited amount of ceric ammonium nitrate (Khand *et al.*, 1974). Thus such oxidation of $PhCH_2 CCo_3 (CO)_9$ in ethanol at room temperature gave $PhCH_2 C{\equiv}CCH_2 Ph$ as major product, along with lesser amounts of $PhCH_2 CO_2 Et$ and $PhCH_2 CHO$, while diphenylacetylene was produced in 25% yield from $PhCCo_3 (CO)_9$.

The oxidation of alkylidynetricobalt nonacarbonyl complexes has been studied by a number of groups. An excess of ceric ammonium nitrate in aqueous acetone serves to oxidize most $RCCo_3(CO)_9$ compounds to the corresponding carboxylic acid, RCO_2H, in high yield, and those complexes which resist such degradation can be oxidized to the acid with potassium permanganate in aqueous acetone (Seyferth *et al.*, 1974a). Hydrogen peroxide may also be used to effect such oxidation (Krüerke and Hübel, 1959).

When selected $RCCo_3(CO)_9$ were heated in alcohol medium in the presence of molecular oxygen, malonic ester derivatives were produced (Tominaga *et al.*, 1970):

$$RCCo_3(CO)_9 \xrightarrow[\substack{O_2 \text{ bubbled in} \\ (40-80\%)}]{R'OH, 70°} RCH(CO_2R')_2 + Co_2O_3 \qquad (142)$$

$$(R = H, CH_3; R' = CH_3; C_2H_5)$$

Molecular halogens also destroy the $RCCo_3(CO)_9$ cluster, giving organic trihalides, e.g. (Krüerke and Hübel, 1959):

$$PhCH_2CCo_3(CO)_9 + Br_2 \xrightarrow{CCl_4} PhCH_2CBr_3 + 3CoBr_2 + 9CO \qquad (143)$$

It was such a degradation by bromine which led to the correct assignment of structure for $RCCo_3(CO)_9$ complexes (Krüerke and Hübel, 1959) a year after their initial discovery (Markby et al., 1958).

Solvolysis and solvolytic carbonylation have also been used to convert various alkylidynetricobalt nonacarbonyl compounds to organic products:

$$CH_3CCo_3(CO)_9 \xrightarrow[\text{(Tominaga et al., 1970)}]{NaOMe/MeOH} CH_3CH(CO_2Me)_2 \qquad (144)$$

$$CH_3CCo_3(CO)_9 \xrightarrow[\substack{C_6H_6 \quad (50\%) \\ \text{(Tominaga et al., 1970)}}]{H_2, CO \text{ (elevated P)}} C_2H_5CHO \qquad (145)$$

$$CH_3CCo_3(CO)_9 \xrightarrow[\text{(Tominaga et al., 1970)}]{n\text{-Bu}_3P, MeOH, 100 \text{ atm } CO} \begin{array}{l} C_2H_5CO_2Me \quad (14\%) \\ + \\ CH_3CH(CO_2Me)_2 \quad (61\%) \\ + \\ (CH_2CO_2Me)_2 \quad (5\%) \end{array} \qquad (146)$$

$$(OC)_9Co_3CH_2CH_2CO_2H \xrightarrow[\text{(Albanesi and Gavezotti, 1966)}]{H_2O} HO_2C(CH_2)_3CO_2H \qquad (147)$$

$$(OC)_9Co_3CCH=CHCO_2H \xrightarrow[\text{(Albanesi and Gavezotti, 1966)}]{H_2O} \begin{array}{l} CH_2=CHCH_2CO_2H \\ + \\ HO_2C(CH_2)_3CO_2H \\ + \\ HO_2CCH_2CH=CHCO_2H \end{array} \qquad (148)$$

Reduction of $RCCo_3(CO)_9$ to the hydrocarbon RCH_3 also is possible. Sodium borohydride in 1,2-dimethoxyethane was found to effect this conversion (Khand et al., 1974):

$$PhCH_2CCo_3(CO)_9 \xrightarrow{NaBH_4/DME} PhCH_2CH_3 \qquad (149)$$

Hydrogenolysis of $HCCo_3(CO)_9$ and $CH_3CCo_3(CO)_9$ was also accomplished by irradiating these complexes in the presence of hydrogen with visible or ultraviolet light (Geoffroy and Epstein, 1977):

$$4HCCo_3(CO)_9 + 6H_2 \xrightarrow{\ h\nu\ } 4CH_4 + 3Co_4(CO)_{12} \qquad (150)$$

Dicobalt octacarbonyl was the cobalt-containing product when the irradiation was carried out in the presence of H_2/CO. Irradiation of CH_3CCo_3-$(CO)_9$ in the presence of hydrogen gave ethylene and ethane in $1.5:1$ ratio.

The $RCCo_3(CO)_9$-to-organic product conversions which have been reported to date are not numerous, and those examples which are cited are relatively simple ones which give simple organic products whose preparation can be effected much more easily by conventional organic procedures. This area of $RCCo_3(CO)_9$ chemistry certainly merits further investigation. Especially of interest will be any procedures which result in efficient trapping of the RĊ: fragment upon degradation of the cluster complex.

D. Applications of Alkylidynetricobalt Nonacarbonyl Complexes as Catalysts in Organic Processes

Catalytic applications of $RCCo_3(CO)_9$ have been sought, and, indeed, several reactions have been found to be "catalyzed" by such cobalt cluster complexes. Catalysis of the hydroformylation of 1- and 2-pentene to give aldehydes in high yields and with a "fairly high normal-to-branched selectivity" was effected by $PhCCo_3(CO)_9$ (Ryan et al., 1977). The reaction conditions were mild, with temperatures ranging from $110°$ to $130°$ and initial pressures of 230–1160 psig. An "opened" cluster cobalt hydride intermediate (XXIII) was suggested. It is important to note that the $PhCCo_3$-$(CO)_9$ catalyst was recovered in high yield upon conclusion of the reaction,

(XXIII)

so it is likely that the cluster complex itself, not one of its dissociation products, such as $Co_2(CO)_8$ or $HCo(CO)_4$ (via reaction with hydrogen), is the active catalytic species.

In another catalytic process, disubstituted acetylenes are trimerized to hexasubstituted benzenes when heated in the presence of alkylidynetricobalt nonacarbonyls (Dickson and Tailby, 1970):

$$PhCCo_3(CO)_9 + CH_3C{\equiv}CCH_3 \xrightarrow[\text{in hexane \ (20\%)}]{160°, \ 35 \ hr} (CH_3)_6C_6 \qquad (151)$$

$$CH_3CCo_3(CO)_9 + PhC{\equiv}CPh \xrightarrow[\ (72\%)]{160°, \ 14 \ hr} Ph_6C_6 \qquad (152)$$

In these reactions it seems likely that the $RCo_3(CO)_9$ complexes are undergoing thermal degradation to give simpler cobalt carbonyl species. The latter then would induce acetylene trimerization through well-established routes. One may note that in some cases acetylene-derived cobalt carbonyl complexes were isolated (Dickson and Tailby, 1970):

$$CH_3O_2CCCo_3(CO)_9 + CH_3C{\equiv}CH \xrightarrow{100°, \ 4 \ hr} (CH_3C_2H)Co_2(CO)_6 \qquad (153)$$

Alkylidynetricobalt nonacarbonyl complexes also have been found to play catalytic roles in processes involving olefin conversions. Thus, various $RCo_3(CO)_9$ compounds have been shown to be initiators of olefin polymerization (Bamford et al., 1964; Pályi et al., 1973). The presence of carbon tetrachloride in 0.001–0.01 M concentration was required in order to obtain good yields. In the initiation of acrylonitrile polymerization, the reactivity of the $RCo_3(CO)_9$ complexes examined was found to be in the order: $R = Cl \simeq H \simeq Br > Ph > F \simeq i - Pr \simeq C_2F_5$ (Pályi et al., 1973). The mechanism of the catalytic processes is not known, but one may consider routes involving chemistry at the apical carbon atom or at the cobalt atom. In support of the former possibility, there is the addition of $HCCo_3(CO)_9$ to the C=C bonds of various olefins which has already been mentioned in Section V,B (Seyferth and Hallgren, 1973; Sakamoto et al., 1973; Kamijo et al., 1973) as well as some reactions of $BrCCo_3(CO)_9$ with olefins (Sakamoto et al., 1973; Kamijo et al., 1973).

$$BrCCo_3(CO)_9 + CH_2{=}CH_2 \longrightarrow C_2H_5CCo_3(CO)_9$$
$$+ CH_3CH{=}C(CH_3)CCo_3(CO)_9 \qquad (154)$$

$$BrCCo_3(CO)_9 + CH_2{=}CHCO_2Me \longrightarrow CH_3O_2CCH_2CH_2CCo_3(CO)_9 \qquad (155)$$

However, while it is possible to rationalize the catalytic action of $HCCo_3$-$(CO)_9$, $BrCCo_3(CO)_9$, and $ClCCo_3(CO)_9$ in terms of such initiation steps, such chemistry will not accommodate the fact that acrylonitrile can be polymerized using $RCCo_3(CO)_9$ initiators where R = Ph, F, Me_2CH, and C_2F_5.

Several groups have reported oligomerization reactions of norbornadiene catalyzed by $RCCo_3(CO)_9$ compounds. Stereospecific catalytic dimerization of norbornadiene to the endo-cis-endo isomer (Binor S) **(XXIV)** was found to occur when this diene was heated at reflux in *n*-octane solution in the presence of $ClCCo_3(CO)_9$ or $BrCCo_3(CO)_9$ (Tominaga *et al.*, 1970; Elder and Robinson, 1975). This process was found to be accelerated by the addition of a Lewis acid such as $BF_3 \cdot Et_2O$ (Catton *et al.*, 1976). Rate measurements established the $RCCo_3(CO)_9$ effectiveness as R = Br $\simeq$ Cl > H > CH_3 > Pr. $CF_3CCo_3(CO)_9$ was ineffective. Replacement of CO ligands in $CH_3CCo_3(CO)_9$ by tertiary phosphines increased the rate of Binor S formation (Hüttel and Forkl, 1972). When norbornadiene was heated in high-boiling solvents in the presence of $RCCo_3(CO)_9$ complexes with R = alkyl or aryl in the absence of a Lewis acid, a mixture of organic products, **(XXV–XXX)**, which did not include Binor S, and insoluble cobalt residues was produced. The exo-trans-exo isomer, **(XXV)**, was the major product together with the exo-trans-endo isomer, **(XXVI)** (Elder and Robinson, 1975).

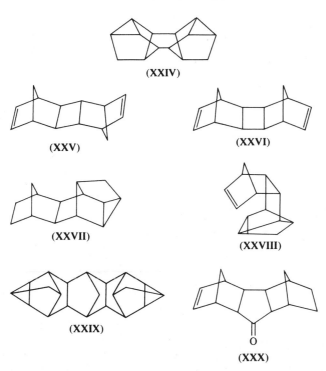

(XXIV)

(XXV)

(XXVI)

(XXVII)

(XXVIII)

(XXIX)

(XXX)

It was suggested (Elder and Robinson, 1975) that stereospecific Binor S formation in some way involves coordination of one molecule of norbornadiene at cobalt and reaction of another molecule of the diene at the apical carbon, thus enabling the operation of Schrauzer's " π-multicenter reaction " pathway. When the apical carbon atom cannot be involved (i.e., when R = alkyl or aryl), then these oligomerizations can only occur via chemistry at cobalt, and nonstereospecific pathways result. The interaction of dienes, including norbornadiene, 1,3-cyclohexadiene, and cyclopentadiene, with $RCCo_3 (CO)_9$ (R = Ph, Me, Et, $MeCO_2$, o-, m-, p-$CH_3C_6H_4$, etc.) has been demonstrated, and complexes of type $RCCo_3 (CO)_7$ (diene) have been isolated and characterized in the case of the first two dienes. With cyclopentadiene, η^5-cyclopentadienyl complexes, $RCCo_3 (CO)_4 (\eta^5\text{-}C_5H_5)_2$, were formed (Elder and Robinson, 1975).

The $RCCo_3(CO)_9$ complexes are easy to prepare and are rather stable, as we have stressed at the beginning of this section. The apical carbon substitutent, R, can be varied widely. We expect catalytic applications of this novel class of cluster complexes to be a fruitful area of study.

ACKNOWLEDGMENT

K. M. Nicholas would like to thank the members of his organometallic class for assistance in the literature search and Dr. D. J. Sardella for helpful comments on the manuscript.

REFERENCES

Aimé, S., Milone, L., and Valle, M. (1976). Inorg. Chim. Acta 18, 9.
Aimé, S., Milone, L., Rossetti, R., and Stanghellini, P. L. (1977). Inorg. Chim. Acta 22, 135.
Albanesi, G., and Gavezotti, E. (1966). Atti Accad. Naz. Lincei, Cl. Sci. Fis., Mat. Nat., Rend. 41, 497.
Bailey, N. A., Churchill, M. R., Hunt, R. L., and Wilkinson, G. (1964). Proc. Chem. Soc., London p. 401.
Bailey, N. A., Hall, S. E., Jotham, R. W., and Kettle, S. F. A. (1971). Chem. Commun. p. 282.
Bamford, C. H., Eastmond, C. G., and Maltman, W. R. (1964). Trans. Faraday Soc. 60, 1432.
Barlex, D. M., Kemmitt, R. D. W., and Littlecott, G. W. (1969). Chem. Commun. p. 613.
Barlex, D. M., Kemmitt, R. D. W., and Littlecott, G. W. (1972). J. Organomet. Chem. 43, 225.
Bennett, M. A., Robertson, G. B., Whimp, P. O., and Yoshida, Y. (1971). J. Am. Chem. Soc. 93, 3797.
Bennett, M. A., Johnson, R. N., Robertson, G. B., Turney, T. W., and Whimp, P. O. (1972). J. Am. Chem. Soc. 94, 6540.
Bladon, P., Khand, I. U., and Pauson, P. L. (1977a). J. Chem. Res. (S) p. 8.

Bladon, P., Khand, I. U., and Pauson, P. L. (1977b). *J. Chem. Res. (M)* p. 153.
Blizzard, A. C., and Santry, D. P. (1968). *J. Am. Chem. Soc.* **90**, 5749.
Bonnemann, H., Brinkmann, R., and Schenkluhn, H. (1974). *Synthesis* p. 575.
Booth, B. L., and Hargreaves, R. G. (1971). *J. Organomet. Chem.* **33**, 365.
Booth, B. L., and Lloyd, A. D. (1972). *J. Organomet. Chem.* **35**, 195.
Bor, G., Markó, L., and Markó, B. (1961). *Acta Chim. Acad. Sci. Hung.* **27**, 395.
Bor, G., Markó, L., and Markó, B. (1962). *Chem. Ber.* **95**, 333.
Boston, J. L., Sharp, D. W. A., and Wilkinson, G. (1962). *J. Chem. Soc.* p. 3488.
Boston, J. L., Grim, S. O., and Wilkinson, G. (1963). *J. Chem. Soc.* p. 3468.
Bowden, F. L., and Lever, A. B. P. (1968). *Organomet. Chem. Rev., Sect. A* **3**, 227.
Bradford, C. W., Nyholm, R. S., Gainsford, G. J., Guss, J. M., Ireland, P. R., and Mason, R. (1972). *Chem. Commun.* p. 87.
Canty, A. J., Johnson, B. F. G., Lewis, J., and Norton, J. R. (1972). *J. Chem. Soc., Chem. Commun.* p. 1331.
Catton, G. A., Jones, G. F. C., Mays, M. J., and Howell, J. A. S. (1976). *Inorg. Chim. Acta* **20**, L41.
Cetini, G., Gambino, O., Rossetti, R., and Sappa, E. (1967). *J. Organomet. Chem.* **8**, 149.
Chatt, J., and Duncanson, L. A. (1953). *J. Chem. Soc.* p. 2939.
Chisholm, M. H., and Clark, H. C. (1971). *Inorg. Chem.* **10**, 2557.
Chisholm, M. H., and Clark, H. C. (1972). *J. Am. Chem. Soc.* **94**, 1532.
Chisholm, M. H., and Clark, H. C. (1973). *Acc. Chem. Res.* **6**, 202.
Chisholm, M. H., Clark, H. C., Manzer, L. E., and Stothers, J. B. (1972). *J. Am. Chem. Soc.* **94**, 5087.
Chukhadzhyan, G. A., Gevorkyan, G. A., and Kukolev, V. P. (1976). *Zh. Obshch. Khim.* **46**, 909.
Clark, H. C., and Hine, K. E. (1976). *J. Organomet. Chem.* **105**, C32.
Clark, H. C., and Manzer, L. E. (1974). *Inorg. Chem.* **13**, 1291.
Clark, H. C., and Puddephatt, R. J. (1971). *Inorg. Chem.* **10**, 18.
Clark, H. C., and von Werner, K. (1975). *J. Organomet. Chem.* **101**, 347.
Clark, H. C., and Wong, C. S. (1975). *J. Organomet. Chem.* **92**, C31.
Clark, H. C., Jablonski, C. R., and Wong, C. S. (1975). *Inorg. Chem.* **14**, 1332.
Collman, J. P., and Kang, J. W. (1967). *J. Am. Chem. Soc.* **89**, 844.
Collman, J. P., Kang, J. W., Little, W. F., and Sullivan, M. F. (1968). *Inorg. Chem.* **7**, 1298.
Connor, R. E., and Nicholas, K. M. (1977). *J. Organomet. Chem.* **125**, C45.
Cook, C. D., and Jauhal, G. S. (1968). *J. Am. Chem. Soc.* **90**, 1464.
Cook, C. D., and Wan, K. Y. (1970). *J. Am. Chem. Soc.* **92**, 2595.
Cramer, R., and Parshall, G. W. (1965). *J. Am. Chem. Soc.* **87**, 1392.
Davidson, G. (1972). *Organomet. Chem. Rev., Sect. A* **8**, 342.
Davidson, J. L., Green, M., Howard, J. A. K., Mann, S. A., Nyathi, J. Z., Stone, F. G. A., and Woodward, P. (1975). *Chem. Commun.* p. 803.
Davies, G. R., Hewerston, W., Mais, R. H. B., Owston, P. G., and Patel, C. G. (1970). *J. Chem. Soc. A* p. 1873.
Deeming, A. J., and Underhill, M. (1973). *J. Chem. Soc., Chem. Commun.* p. 277.
Deeming, A. J., and Underhill, M. (1974). *J. Chem. Soc., Dalton Trans.* p. 1415.
Deeming, A. J., Kimber, R. E., and Underhill, M. (1973). *J. Chem. Soc., Dalton Trans.* **25**, 89.
Deeming, A. J., Hasso, S., Underhill, M., Canty, A. J., Johnson, B. F. G., Jackson, W. G., Lewis, J., and Matheson, T. W. (1974). *J. Chem. Soc., Chem. Commun.* p. 807.
Dent, W. T., Duncanson, L. A., Guy, R. G., Reed, H. W. B., and Shaw, B. L. (1961). *Proc. Chem. Soc., London* p. 169.
Descoins, C., and Samain, D. (1976). *Tetrahedron Lett.* p. 745.

Dewar, M. J. S. (1951). *Bull. Soc. Chim. Fr.* **18**, C71.
Dickson, R. S., and Fraser, P. J. (1974). *Adv. Organomet. Chem.* **12**, 323.
Dickson, R. S., and Tailby, G. R. (1970). *Aust. J. Chem.* **23**, 229.
Dolby, R., and Robinson, B. H. (1972). *J. Chem. Soc., Dalton Trans.* p. 2046.
Dolby, R., and Robinson, B. H. (1973). *J. Chem. Soc., Dalton Trans.* p. 1794.
Elder, P. A., and Robinson, B. H. (1975). *J. Chem. Soc., Dalton Trans.* p. 1771.
Ercoli, R. (1962). *Chim. Ind. (Milan)* **44**, 565.
Ercoli, R., Santambrogio, E., and Tettamanti-Casagrande, G. (1962). *Chim. Ind. (Milan)* **44**, 1344.
Ferraris, R. P., and Gervasio, G. (1974). *J. Chem. Soc., Dalton Trans.* p. 1813.
Fischer, E. O. (1976). *Adv. Organomet. Chem.* **14**, 1.
Fischer, E. O., and Däweritz, A. (1975). *Angew. Chem.* **87**, 360.
Fischer, E. O., Kreis, G., Kreiter, C. G., Müller, J., Huttner, G., and Lorenz, H. (1973). *Angew. Chem.* **85**, 618.
Funk, R. L., and Vollhardt, K. P. C. (1976). *J. Am. Chem. Soc.* **98**, 6755.
Geoffroy, G. L., and Epstein, R. A. (1977). *Inorg. Chem.* **16**, 2795.
Gilchrist, T. L., Graveling, F. J., and Rees, C. W. (1968). *Chem. Commun.* p. 821.
Glanville, J. O., Stewart, J. M., and Grim, S. O. (1967). *J. Organomet. Chem.* **7**, P9.
"Gmelin Handbook of Inorganic Chemistry," (1973). 8th ed., New Suppl. Ser., Vol. 6, Part II, p. 145. Verlag Chemie, Weinheim.
Gowling, E. W., Kettle, S. F. A., and Sharples, G. M. (1968). *Chem. Commun.* p. 21.
Guthrie, D. J. S., Khand, I. U., Knox, G. R., Kollmeier, J., Pauson, P. L., and Watts, W. E. (1975). *J. Organomet. Chem.* **90**, 93.
Hart, D. W., and Schwartz, J. (1974). *J. Am. Chem. Soc.* **96**, 8115.
Hart, D. W., Blackburn, T. F., and Schwartz, J. (1975). *J. Am. Chem. Soc.* **97**, 679.
Hartley, F. R. (1969). *Chem. Rev.* **69**, 799.
Herberhold, M., Alt, H., and Kreiter, C. G. (1976). *Justus Liebigs Ann. Chem.* p. 300.
Hillard, R. L., III, and Vollhardt, K. P. C. (1975). *Angew. Chem., Int. Ed. Engl.* **14**, 712.
Hillard, R. L., III, and Vollhardt, K. P. C. (1977). *J. Am. Chem. Soc.* (in press).
Hodes, H. D., and Nicholas, K. M. unpublished results.
Hoogzand, C., and Hübel, W. (1968). *In* "Organic Synthesis via Metal Carbonyls," (I. Wender and P. Pino, eds.), Vol. 1, p. 343. Wiley, New York.
Hosokawa, T., and Moritani, I. (1969). *Tetrahedron Lett.* p. 302.
Hübel, W. (1968). *In* "Organic Synthesis via Metal Carbonyls" (I. Wender and P. Pino, eds.), Vol. 1, p. 273. Wiley, New York.
Hübel, W., and Merenyi, R. (1964). *J. Organomet. Chem.* **2**, 213.
Hunt, R. L., and Wilkinson, G. (1965). *Inorg. Chem.* **4**, 1270.
Hüttel, R., and Forkl, H. (1972). *Chem. Ber.* **105**, 1663.
Ito, T., Hasegawa, S., Takahashi, T., and Ishii, Y. (1972). *Chem. Commun.* p. 629.
Iwashita, Y., Ishikawa, A., and Kainosho, M. (1971). *Spectrochim. Acta, Part A* **27**, 271.
Iwashita, Y., Tamura, F., and Wakamatsu, H. (1973). *Bull. Chem. Soc. Jpn.* **43**, 1520.
Johnson, A. W. (1946). "The Chemistry of Acetylenic Compounds," Vol. 1, p. 56. Arnold, London.
Johnson, B. F. G., Lewis, J., and Schorpp, K. T. (1975). *J. Organomet. Chem.* **91**, C13.
Kamijo, T., Kitamura, T., Sakamoto, N., and Joh, T. (1973). *J. Organomet. Chem.* **54**, 265.
Kemmitt, R. D. W., Kimura, B. Y., and Littlecott, G. W. (1973). *J. Chem. Soc., Dalton Trans.* p. 636.
Khand, I. U., and Pauson, P. L. (1974). *Chem. Commun.* p. 379.
Khand, I. U., and Pauson, P. L. (1976). *J. Chem. Soc., Perkin Trans. 1* p. 30.

Khand, I. U., and Pauson, P. L. (1977a). *J. Chem. Res. (S)* p. 9.
Khand, I. U., and Pauson, P. L. (1977b). *J. Chem. Res. (M)* p. 168.
Khand, I. U., Knox, G. R., Pauson, P. L., and Watts, W. E. (1974). *J. Organomet. Chem.* **73**, 383.
Klinger, R. J., Butler, W., and Curtis, M. D. (1975). *J. Am. Chem. Soc.* **97**, 3535.
Krüerke, U., and Hübel, W. (1959). *Chem. Ind. (London)* p. 1264.
Krüerke, U., and Hübel, W. (1961). *Chem. Ber.* **94**, 2829.
Krüerke, U., Hoogzand, C., and Hübel, W. (1961). *Chem. Ber.* **94**, 2817.
Labinger, J. A., and Schwartz, J. (1975). *J. Am. Chem. Soc.* **97**, 1596.
Labinger, J. A., Schwartz, J., and Townsend, J. M. (1974). *J. Am. Chem. Soc.* **96**, 4009.
Lockwood, R., and Nicholas, K. M. (1977). *Tetrahedron Lett.* p. 4163.
McClure, G. L., and Baddley, W. H. (1970). *J. Organomet. Chem.* **25**, 261.
Maitlis, P. M. (1971a). "The Organic Chemistry of Palladium," Vol. 1, pp. 110–130. Academic Press, New York.
Maitlis, P. M. (1971b). "The Organic Chemistry of Palladium," Vol. 1, pp. 171–172. Academic Press, New York.
Maitlis, P. M. (1971c). "The Organic Chemistry of Palladium," Vol. 2, pp. 31 and 47–58. Academic Press, New York.
Maitlis, P. M. (1976). *Acc. Chem. Res.* **9**, 93.
Malatesta, L., Santarella, G., Vallarino, L. M., and Zingales, F. (1960). *Angew. Chem.* **72**, 34.
Mann, B. E., Shaw, B. L., and Tucker, N. I. (1971). *J. Chem. Soc. A* p. 2667.
Markby, R., Wender, I., Friedel, R. A., Cotton, F. A., and Sternberg, H. W. (1958). *J. Am. Chem. Soc.* **80**, 6529.
Messeguer, A., Serratosa, F., and Rivera, J. (1973). *Tetrahedron Lett.* p. 2895.
Michman, M., and Balog, M. (1971). *J. Organomet. Chem.* **31**, 395.
Mills, O. S., and Robinson, G. (1959). *Proc. Chem. Soc., London* p. 156.
Mills, O. S., and Robinson, G. (1967). *Inorg. Chim. Acta* **1**, 61.
Müller, E., and Beissner, C. (1973). *Chem.-Ztg.* **97**, 207.
Müller, E., and Dilger, W. (1973). *Chem.-Ztg.* **97**, 388.
Müller, E., and Odenigbo, G. (1975). *Justus Liebigs Ann. Chem.* p. 1435.
Müller, E., and Segnitz, A. (1973). *Justus Liebigs Ann. Chem.* p. 1583.
Müller, E., and Winter, W. (1975). *Justus Liebigs Ann. Chem.* p. 605.
Müller, E., Beissner, C., Jackle, H., Langer, E., Muhm, H., Odenigbo, G., Sauerbier, M., Segnitz, A., Streichfuss, D., and Thomas, R. (1971). *Justus Liebigs Ann. Chem.* **754**, 64.
Müller, E., Lupold, E., and Winter, W. (1975). *Chem. Ber.* **108**, 237.
Nakamura, A., and Hagihara, N. (1963). *Nippon Kagaku Zasshi* **84**, 344.
Nakamura, A., and Otsuka, S. (1972). *J. Am. Chem. Soc.* **94**, 1886.
Nelson, J. H., and Jonassen, H. B. (1971). *Coord. Chem. Rev.* **6**, 27.
Nesmeyanov, A. N., Anisimov, K. N., Kolobova, N. E., and Pasynskii, A. A. (1969a). *Izv. Akad. Nauk SSSR, Ser. Khim.* p. 100.
Nesmeyanov, A. N., Anisimov, K. N., Kolobova, N. E., and Pasynskii, A. A. (1969b). *Izv. Akad. Nauk SSSR, Ser. Khim.* p. 183.
Nesmeyanov, A. N., Kolobova, N. E., Skripkin, V. V., and Anisimov, K. N. (1971). *Dokl. Akad. Nauk SSSR* **196**, 606.
Nicholas, K. M., and Pettit, R. (1971). *Tetrahedron Lett.* p. 3475.
Nicholas, K. M., and Pettit, R. (1972). *J. Organomet. Chem.* **44**, C21.
Otsuka, S., and Nakamura, A. (1976a). *Adv. Organomet. Chem.* **14**, 245.
Otsuka, S., and Nakamura, A. (1976b). *Adv. Organomet. Chem.* **14**, 247–249.
Pályi, G., Piacenti, F., and Markó, L. (1970). *Inorg. Chim. Acta, Rev.* **4**, 109.
Pályi, G., Baumgartner, F., and Czajlik, I. (1973). *J. Organomet. Chem.* **49**, C85.

Pályi, G., Varadi, G., Vizi-Orosz, A., and Markó, L. (1975). *J. Organomet. Chem.* **90**, 85.
Pauson, P. L., Watts, W. E., and Foreman, M. I. (1973). *J. Chem. Soc., Perkin Trans. 1* p. 977.
Penfold, B. R., and Robinson, B. H. (1973). *Acc. Chem. Res.* **6**, 73.
Pollock, D. F., and Maitlis, P. M. (1966). *Can. J. Chem.* **44**, 2673.
Reppe, W., and Schweckendiek, W. J. (1948). *Justus Liebigs Ann. Chem.* **560**, 104.
Robertson, G. B., and Whimp, P. O. (1971). *J. Organomet. Chem.* **32**, C69.
Robinson, B. H., and Spencer, J. L. (1971). *J. Chem. Soc. A* p. 2045.
Roe, D. M., and Massey, A. G. (1970). *J. Organomet. Chem.* **23**, 547.
Ryan, R. C., Pittman, C. U., Jr., and O'Connor, J. P. (1977). *J. Am. Chem. Soc.* **99**, 1986.
Sakamoto, N., Kitamura, T., and Joh, T. (1973). *Chem. Lett.* p. 583.
Sauer, J. C., Cramer, R. D., Engelhardt, V. A., Ford, T. A., Holmquist, H. E., and Howk, B. W. (1959). *J. Am. Chem. Soc.* **81**, 3677.
Schwartz, J., Hart, D. W., and Holden, J. L. (1972). *J. Am. Chem. Soc.* **94**, 9269.
Sears, C. T., Jr., and Stone, F. G. A. (1968). *J. Organomet. Chem.* **11**, 644.
Segal, J. A., and Johnson, B. F. G. (1975). *J. Chem. Soc., Dalton Trans.* p. 1990.
Seyferth, D. (1976). *Adv. Organomet. Chem.* **14**, 97.
Seyferth, D., and Hallgren, J. E. (1973). *J. Organomet. Chem.* **49**, C41.
Seyferth, D., and Nivert, C. L. (1976). *J. Organomet. Chem.* **113**, C65.
Seyferth, D., and Nivert, C. L., (1977a) *J. Am. Chem. Soc.* **99**, 5209.
Seyferth, D., and Nivert, C. L. (1977b). To be published.
Seyferth, D., and Wehman, A. T. (1970). *J. Am. Chem. Soc.* **92**, 5520.
Seyferth, D., and White, D. L. (1971). *J. Organomet. Chem.* **32**, 317.
Seyferth, D., Hallgren, J. E., Spohn, R. J., Wehman, A. T., and Williams, G. H. (1971). *Spec. Lect., Int. Congr. Pure Appl. Chem., 23rd, 1971* Vol. 6, p. 133.
Seyferth, D., Hallgren, J. E., and Hung, P. L. K. (1973a). *J. Organomet. Chem.* **50**, 265.
Seyferth, D., Williams, G. H., and Hallgren, J. E. (1973b). *J. Am. Chem. Soc.* **95**, 266.
Seyferth, D., Hallgren, J. E., Spohn, R. J., Williams, G. H., Nestle, M. O., and Hung, P. L. K. (1974a). *J. Organomet. Chem.* **65**, 99.
Seyferth, D., Williams, G. H., Hung, P. L. K., and Hallgren, J. E. (1974b). *J. Organomet. Chem.* **71**, 97.
Seyferth, D., Williams, G. H., and Traficante, D. D. (1974c). *J. Am. Chem. Soc.* **96**, 604.
Seyferth, D., Eschbach, C. S., Williams, G. H., Hung, P. L. K., and Cheng, Y. M. (1974d). *J. Organomet. Chem.* **78**, C13.
Seyferth, D., Hallgren, J. E., and Eschbach, C. S. (1974e). *J. Am. Chem. Soc.* **96**, 1730.
Seyferth, D., Eschbach, C. S., and Nestle, M. O. (1975a). *J. Organomet. Chem.* **97**, C11.
Seyferth, D., Williams, G. H., Wehman, A. T., and Nestle, M. O. (1975b). *J. Am. Chem. Soc.* **97**, 2107.
Seyferth, D., Nestle, M. O., and Wehman, A. T. (1975c). *J. Am. Chem. Soc.* **97**, 7414.
Seyferth, D., Nestle, M. O., and Eschbach, C. S. (1976). *J. Am. Chem. Soc.* **98**, 6724.
Seyferth, D., Williams, G. H., and Nivert, C. L. (1977a). *Inorg. Chem.* **16**, 758.
Seyferth, D., Eschbach, C. S., Williams, G. H., and Hung, P. L. K. (1977b). *J. Organomet. Chem.* **134**, 67.
Sly, W. G. (1959). *J. Am. Chem. Soc.* **81**, 18.
Sternberg, H. W., Greenfield, H., Friedel, R. A., Wotiz, J., Markby, R., and Wender, I. (1954). *J. Am. Chem. Soc.* **76**, 1457.
Sternberg, H., Shukys, J. O., Donne, C., Markby, R., Friedel, R., and Wender, I. (1959). *J. Am. Chem. Soc.* **81**, 2339.
Straub, H., Huth, A., and Müller, E. (1973). *Synthesis* p. 783.
Strohmeier, W., and von Hobe, D. (1961). *Z. Naturforsch., Teil B* **16**, 402.

Suzuki, Y., and Takizawa, T. (1972). *Chem. Commun.* p. 837.
Tate, D. P., and Augl, J. M. (1963). *J. Am. Chem. Soc.* **85**, 2174.
Tate, D. P., Augl, J. M., Ritchey, W. M., Ross, B. L., and Grasselli, J. G. (1964). *J. Am. Chem. Soc.* **86**, 3261.
Thomas, J. L. (1973). *J. Am. Chem. Soc.* **95**, 1838.
Tilney-Bassett, J. F. (1961). *J. Chem. Soc.* p. 577.
Tirpak, M. R., Holligsworth, C. A., and Wotiz, J. H. (1960). *J. Org. Chem.* **25**, 687.
Todd, L. J., and Wilkinson, J. R. (1974). *J. Organomet. Chem.* **80**, C31.
Tominaga, K., Yamagami, N., and Wakamatsu, H. (1970). *Tetrahedron Lett.* p. 2217.
Tripathy, P. B., and Roundhill, D. M. (1970). *J. Am. Chem. Soc.* **92**, 3825.
Tsumura, R., and Hagihara, N. (1965). *Bull. Chem. Soc. Jpn.* **38**, 1901.
Vollhardt, K. P. C. (1977). *Acc. Chem. Res.* **10**, 1.
Voyevodskaya, T. I., Pribytkova, I. M., and Ustynyuk, Yu. A. (1972). *J. Organomet. Chem.* **37**, 187.
Wakatsuki, Y., and Yamazaki, H. (1973). *Chem. Commun.* p. 280.
Wakatsuki, Y., Yamazaki, H., and Iwasaki, H. (1973). *J. Am. Chem. Soc.* **95**, 5781.
Wakatsuki, T., Kuramitsu, T., and Yamazaki, H. (1974a). *Tetrahedron Lett.* p. 4549.
Wakatsuki, Y., Aoki, K., and Yamazaki, H. (1974b). *J. Am. Chem. Soc.* **96**, 5284.
Wong, K. L. T., Thomas, J. L., and Brintzinger, H. H. (1974). *J. Am. Chem. Soc.* **96**, 3694.
Yamazaki, H., and Hagihara, N. (1967). *J. Organomet. Chem.* **7**, 22.
Yamazaki, H., Aoki, K., Yamamoto, Y., and Wakatsuki, Y. (1975). *J. Am. Chem. Soc.* **97**, 3546.
Zeiss, H. H., and Tsutsui, M. (1959). *J. Am. Chem. Soc.* **81**, 6090.

2

ARENE COMPLEXES IN ORGANIC SYNTHESIS

GÉRARD JAOUEN

65

Copyright © 1978 by Academic Press, Inc.
All rights of reproduction in any form reserved.
ISBN 0-12-053102-X

I. INTRODUCTION

Sigma- and π-arene complexes of transition metals are useful catalysts, reagents, and intermediates in organic synthesis. Catalytic applications of these complexes have been reviewed (Andretta et al., 1970; Harmon et al., 1973; Dolcetti and Hoffman, 1974; James, 1973). This chapter will emphasize the stoichiometric reactions of arene complexes.

One of the first examples utilizing arene complexes in synthesis was reported by Birch et al. in 1965. 1-Methoxy-1,3-cyclohexadiene and several steroid derivatives could be transformed into aromatic compounds via arene metal carbonyl complexes. Numerous other examples have been reported in the literature since the publication of this paper.

The general method for these stoichiometric syntheses consists of (1) complexation of the aromatic moiety by a transition metal; (2) utilization of any alteration in steric and electronic factors, or in the symmetry of the ligand, in effecting the desired reaction; and (3) cleavage of the metal–ligand bond and isolation of the organic product.

The prerequisites (e.g., efficient decomplexation methods) which must be met in order to make this reaction sequence useful are the same as those for olefin complexes (see Birch and Jenkins, Vol. 1, Ch. 1, Secs. I and II). Complexation reactions of arenes have been reviewed recently by Silverthorn (1975).

II. ARENE LIGANDS AS DISPLACING AGENTS   IN ORGANOMETALLIC COMPLEXES

It is possible to replace one complexed arene ligand by another if the reactant complex contains a weak metal–ligand bond, while the competing ligand constitutes a center richer in electron density. In the benchrotrene series, this type of exchange generally requires high temperatures and results in poor yields (Zeiss et al., 1966; Rubezhov and Gubin, 1972). However, it has recently been shown (Meyer and Jaouen, 1975; Goasmat et al., 1975) that, by creation of a carbonium ion α to the complexed ring, the metal–arene bond is sufficiently weakened to allow ligand transfer to occur under mild conditions. Unfortunately, no asymmetric induction was observed during this transfer (Meyer and Jaouen, 1975).

In a similar manner (Munro and Pauson, 1961) have shown that displacement of the six-electron ligand from (cycloheptatriene) chromium tricarbonyl may be accomplished without difficulty in the presence of arenes. Howell *et al.* (1974) have utilized this property in the synthesis of azulenes by *in situ* liberation of heptafulvenes in the presence of dienophiles. Thus, reaction of the dimethyl ester of acetylenedicarboxylic acid **(I)** with several monosubstituted heptafulvene chromium tricarbonyl derivatives **(IIa–c)** in refluxing xylene gives the azulenes **(III)**. The latter are formed by dehydrogenation of the initial Diels–Alder adduct at the reflux temperature. For the disubstituted compound **(IId)**, where such a dehydrogenation is not possible, the Diels–Alder adduct **(IV)** is obtained. No dehydrogenation is found if the lower boiling benzene is used as solvent; thus, the adduct **V** may

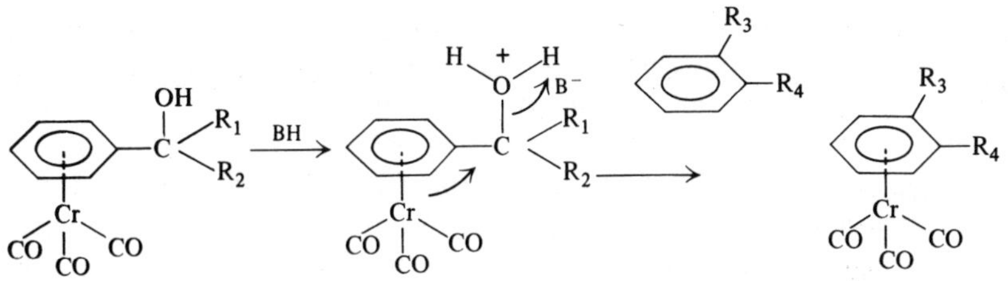

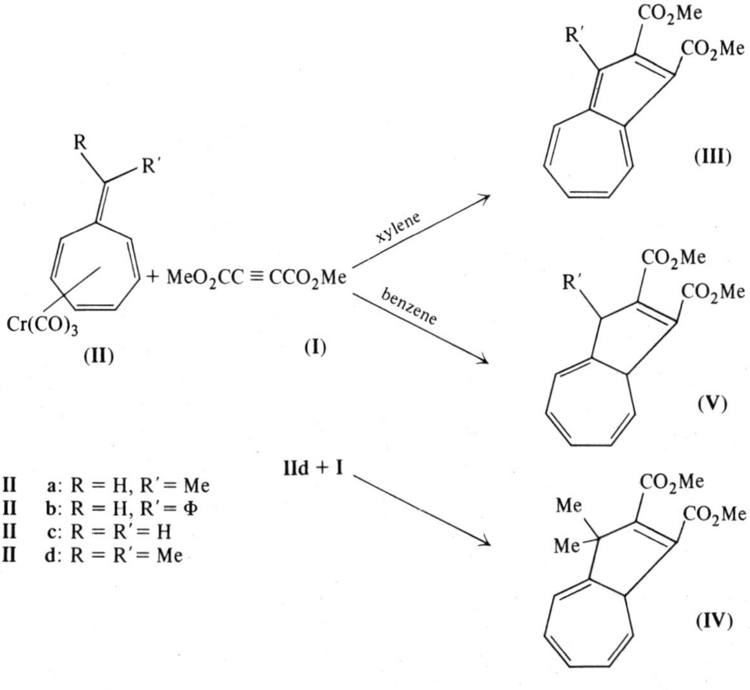

II   a: R = H, R′ = Me
II   b: R = H, R′ = Φ
II   c: R = R′ = H
II   d: R = R′ = Me

be obtained from complex **IIb**. However, the authors conclude that a disso-
ciative mechanism involving loss of the $Cr(CO)_3$ group is operative, rather
than an arene displacement of the heptafulvene.

   Finally, Kutney *et al.* (1974) and Kutney (1977) have utilized the displacement by pyridine of the $Cr(CO)_3$ group from complexes of dihydropyridines.
This displacement provides access to unstable dihydropyridines which are of
considerable interest in natural products and in biosynthetic processes (Bear
et al., 1973). The 1,2- and 1,6-dihydropyridines **(VII)** and **(VIII)** were prepared
in situ by reduction of *N*-methyl-3-ethylpyridinium iodide with $NaBH_4$ in
basic methanol solution. The possibility of dihydropyridine complexation
using the $Cr(CO)_3$ group has previously been mentioned by Ofele (1967;
Fischer and Ofele, 1967) and in the present case, is easily accomplished using
$(CH_3CN)_3Cr(CO)_3$. Thus, the compounds *N*-methyl-3-ethyl-1,2-dihydro-
pyridine **(IX)** and *N*-methyl-3-ethyl-1,6-dihydropyridine **(X)** may be isolated
without risk of isomerization.

   Liberation of the dihydropyridine may then be performed by exchange
with pyridine at room temperature. The 1,2-dihydropyridine may be used
without isolation, although the product prepared by direct reduction of the
pyridinium salt may be used with equal success. On the contrary, other
synthetic approaches to pure 1,6-dihydropyridines have been unsuccessful,
and intermediate complexation by $Cr(CO)_3$ constitutes the sole means of
access to these heterocycles.

   The preceding examples have been concerned with reactive organic
species complexed by the $Cr(CO)_3$ group. There are, however, many
examples of complexation of stable organic species such as the benzene
moiety, but a discussion of the influence of the complexing group is worthwhile before considering this topic.

III. ELECTRONIC INFLUENCE OF THE Cr(CO)$_3$ GROUP

The nature of the arene–Cr(CO)$_3$ bond has been the subject of many discussions in the last few years. On the basis of arguments drawn from studies of reactivity (Nicholls and Whiting, 1959; Kursanov et al., 1970, 1972; Ashraf, 1972; Jaouen et al., 1972a; Alper et al., 1973), measurements of dissociation constants (Jaouen et al., 1972a; Ashraf and Jackson, 1972; Fischer et al., 1958), and dipole moments (Fischer and Schreiner, 1959), molecular orbital calculations (Carroll and McGlynn, 1968; Brown and Rawlinson, 1969; Saillard et al., 1974), and nmr chemical shifts (Price and Sorensen, 1968; McFarlane and Grim, 1966; Emanuel and Randall, 1969; Fritz and Kreiter, 1967), a strong electron-attracting character, comparable sometimes to a para nitro group, has been postulated for the complexed Cr(CO)$_3$ group. In contrast, it has been shown by other means that the transmission of resonance effects in arene complexes is unchanged when compared with the free ligand (Wu et al., 1971, 1972; Brown and Sloan, 1962; Brown and Carroll, 1965), while the great stability of carbonium ions α to the complexed moiety has been explained in terms of the electron-donating character of the Cr(CO)$_3$ group (Holmes et al., 1965; Trahanovsky and Wells, 1969). This apparent contradiction has been reconciled by Gubin et al., in a series of recent studies (Khandkarova and Gubin, 1970; Gubin and Khandkarova, 1970; Khandkarova et al., 1970; Gubin et al., 1974; Kreindlin et al., 1975). These authors have measured a series of σ constants for the C$_6$H$_5$Cr(CO)$_3$ (BCT) group, and have compared them to those obtained for the free C$_6$H$_5$ group. Several of these values are listed in Table I.

TABLE I

Compounds $\diagdown$ Constants	σ_i	σ^*	σ_p	σ_p^+	σ_p^-
BCT	+0.21	+1.96	+0.18 +0.23	−0.15	+0.29
C$_6$H$_5$	+0.09	+0.60	−0.01	−0.179	+0.09

Thus, a significant difference in the aromatic inductive constant (σ_i) is observed. On the other hand, the aromatic electrophilic constant (σ_p^+) is only slightly lowered by complexation. Comparison of the aromatic nucleophilic constants (σ_p^-) shows that the (C$_6$H$_5$)Cr(CO)$_3$ substituent is a much better electron-attracting group than the free phenyl group. Comparison of the Hammett constants σ_p and σ_p^- demonstrates that the (C$_6$H$_5$)Cr(CO)$_3$

group has the possibility of entering into direct polar conjugation with a donating reaction center (+R).

An explanation for these different effects may be found in the postulate that complexation by $Cr(CO)_3$ results in a net diminution in σ-electron density on the aromatic skeleton, while little perturbation of the π-electron density of the ring occurs (Gubin et al., 1974; Neuse, 1975). A slight weakening of the C–C bonds and a greater rigidity in the plane of the ring have been observed (Caillet and Jaouen, 1975). This is compatible with the fact that, contrary to resonance effects, the transmission of inductive effects in the arene skeleton itself is diminished (Bodner and Todd, 1974; Fletcher and McGlinchey, 1975). A participation by the chromium in σ-π conjugation in the arene ring (Jaouen and Simonneaux, 1973) or an increased polarization of the π-electrons of the complexed moiety (Saillard et al., 1974; Kreindlin et al., 1975) may also be invoked to explain these resonance effects. In an attempt to furnish a simple picture Gubin has compared the effects of the $(C_6H_5)Cr(CO)_3$ substituent to those of the halogen group (Kreindlin et al., 1975). In a manner analogous to the halogens, the $(C_6H_5)Cr(CO)_3$ group provides a strong attractive inductive effect and a resonance effect whose magnitude greatly depends on the nature of the reactive center.

Thus, complexation results in a modification of both the reactivity of the ring itself and of its attached substituents. These changes in properties are particularly significant with respect to applications in organic synthesis.

IV. SIDE-CHAIN REACTIONS OF A RING COMPLEXED BY $Cr(CO)_3$

A great deal of kinetic information is available concerning the effect of complexation of an arene ligand Ar—R on the behavior of the substituent R. As these effects are sometimes contradictory, it is necessary to discuss them according to the type of reaction involved.

A. S_N1 Reactions

Reactions in which the α carbon possesses a carbonium ion type structure in the transition state are greatly accelerated by complexation. Ionization reactions of benzylic derivatives, i.e., the solvolysis of chlorides (Holmes et al., 1965) or the isomerization of thiocyanates or isothiocyanates (Ceccon, 1971), are accelerated by a factor of 10^4–10^5. This extraordinary donating effect of the $Cr(CO)_3$ group has been interpreted either as a direct interaction of a filled metal d orbital with the empty carbon p orbital, or as metal–

carbon hyperconjugation (σ-π delocalization) (Davis et al., 1971; Bly et al., 1970; Bly and Veazey, 1969). It may be noted, however, that in a similar series, that of ferrocene, where the mode of stabilization of metallocenyl carbonium ions has been the subject of much controversy, a recent study has postulated delocalization of the effective positive charge over the entire metallocenyl entity (Braun and Watts, 1975; Koridze et al., 1975).

B. S_N2 Reactions

In S_N2 displacement reactions at a saturated carbon atom in aprotic solvents, the total influence of the $Cr(CO)_3$ group varies with the site of nucleophilic attack, i.e., whether the α or β carbon atom is implicated in the reaction. In the thiocyanate substitution reaction with 2-phenylethyl chloride in acetone (β attack), the increase in rate due to complexation is comparable to that of a p-nitro group ($k_{Cr(CO)_3}/k_H = 2.3$; $k_{NO_2}/k_H = 2.7$) (Ceccon and Sartori, 1973). This is in accord with the similarity in pK_a of p-nitrophenylacetic acid (Nicholls and Whiting, 1959). However, while the same reaction may be effected at the α-position of benzyl chloride, a decrease in rate is observed ($k_{Cr(CO)_3}/k_H = 0.30$) (Ceccon and Sartori, 1973). Similarly, (benzoic acid)chromium tricarbonyl is a significantly weaker acid than p-nitrobenzoic acid (Nicholls and Whiting, 1959). In these two cases, this diminution in reactivity has been interpreted in terms of a large steric effect of the $Cr(CO)_3$ group which may interfere with the solvation of products or the approach of the reactive nucleophile.

C. E2 Reactions

The effect of the electron-attracting character of the $Cr(CO)_3$ group on E2 processes has been examined using the base-catalyzed 1,2-elimination of 2-phenylethyl compounds in alcoholic media to give styrenes. In the transition state of these reactions, the α-carbon has, in effect, a carbanionic character (Bunnett, 1962) although the negative charge may be delocalized into the ring by inductive and/or resonance effects. The results obtained with substrates of the type 2-phenylethylbromide and the corresponding tosylates have shown a fundamental difference between the kinetic effects of the $Cr(CO)_3$ and para nitro groups (Ceccon and Biserni, 1972). In fact, the results suggest that, unlike the para nitro group, the nature of the attractive effect of the $Cr(CO)_3$ group is almost exclusively inductive, and that this species has little capacity for the delocalization of negative charge by resonance. This is in agreement with the ideas developed by Gubin et al.

Complexation results in activation by a factor of the order of 10^2 with respect to development of a carbanion center α to the ring (Ceccon and Catelani, 1974; Ceccon, 1974). However, for a series of free ligands (benzyl chlorides) where the transition states range between well-defined S_N1 and S_N2 character, complexation produces a shift toward a carbonium ion-type transition state (Ceccon and Sartori, 1973). The donor character of the $Cr(CO)_3$ group outweighs its acceptor character.

V. USE OF CHROMIUM CARBONYL GROUPS FOR THE SELECTIVE ACTIVATION OF AROMATIC SIDE CHAINS

Of the two contrasting properties of the $Cr(CO)_3$ group, i.e., donor and acceptor, with respect to an aromatic side-chain, the inductive acceptor effect has been more widely explored with regard to its synthetic consequences. In particular, temporary complexation of an organic substrate favors proton abstraction from a carbon chain in basic media. This increased tendency toward anion formation thus permits the alkylation of substrates whose free ligands have little or no reactivity.

Consider, for example, the remarkable difference in reactivity toward alkylating agents of free and complexed methyl phenylacetate (XI) (Jaouen, 1973). While the free ligand is practically inert to NaH and CH_3I (DMF, 25°), the chromium tricarbonyl complex (XI) rapidly yields (5 min) $[C_6H_5-C(CH_3)_2-CO_2CH_3]Cr(CO)_3$ (XII) (97%) under identical conditions. This property may be used in the formation of small rings at the carbon α to the aromatic ring. The sequence described below (XI → XIII → XIV) has been carried out with an overall yield of 87%, including photochemical decomplexation in air.

$$(CO_3) - Cr - Ph - \overset{\overset{\displaystyle CH_3}{|}}{\underset{\underset{\displaystyle CH_3}{|}}{C}} - CO_2Me$$

(XII)

(XI)   (XIII)   (XIV)

More recently, des Abbayes and Boudeville (1977) have used this type of arylacetic ester alkylation in the synthesis of pharmacologically important compounds. In all the models studied, it was possible to increase temporarily the acidity of the hydrogen atom α to the ester function by the use of a complexation procedure (Table II). The yields are quantitative.

TABLE II

RX	Subtrates
CH_3I	$BCTCH(CH_3)CO_2CH_3$
$C_6H_5CH_2Br$	
$CH_2 = CH - CH_2Br$	
$CH \equiv C - CH_2Br$	
$BrCH_2CO_2CH_3$	

In addition, it has been shown that the generation of enolates by phase transfer catalysis (Jonczyk et al., 1973) sometimes gives poorer yields than the above method using sodium hydride because of a competing saponification reaction.

Another example of the activating effect of the $Cr(CO)_3$ group may be seen in the rapid conversion of (acetophenone)$Cr(CO)_3$ **(XV)** to (isopropylphenylketone)$Cr(CO)_3$ **(XVI)** in DMF using CH_3I (NaH, 25°, 15 min, 90%) (Jaouen et al., 1975). No clean reaction occurs with the free ligand under identical conditions. (Isopropylphenylketone)$Cr(CO)_3$ **(XVI)** may also be obtained starting with (ethylphenylketone)$Cr(CO)_3$ **(XV)**, while (*tert*-butylphenylketone)$Cr(CO)_3$ **(XVII)** may similarly be prepared from any of the ketone complexes previously described, but using DMSO as

$R_1 = H, R_2 = H$ or (and) CH_3
$R_3 = CH_3$
*$BCT = (C_6H_5) Cr(CO)_3$

solvent and t-BuOK as base. These reactions are free from secondary products, as are the decomplexation reactions of the ketones themselves. Thus, from a preparative viewpoint, isolation of the complexes is not necessary.

In the preceding examples, the attracting ketone and ester groups also favor these alkylation reactions, and it is difficult to isolate the effect of the $Cr(CO)_3$ group alone. However, Trahanovsky and Card (1972) have succeeded in deuterating the benzylic position of the complexed ring of $BCTCH_2CH_2CH_2CH_2Ph$ (XVIII) in less than 15 min (using t-BuOK and DMSO-d_6).

$$BCT - CH_2 - (CH_2)_3 - Ph \xrightarrow[DMSO - d_6]{t-BuOK} BCT - CD_2 - (CH_2)_3 - Ph \xrightarrow{Ce^{4+}}$$
$$\text{(XVIII)} \qquad\qquad\qquad\qquad \text{(XIX)}$$

$$C_6H_5 - CD_2 - (CH_2)_3 - Ph$$
$$\text{(XX)}$$

Furthermore, under similar conditions, isopropylbenzene may be obtained starting from $BCTCH_2CH_3$, although some contamination with $tert$-butylbenzene is observed (Jaouen et al., 1975).

The degree of activation of the complexed ligand may further be modified by the transformation of $Cr(CO)_3$ into $Cr(CO)_2L$, where L is another two-electron donor ligand such as thiocarbonyl, phosphine, or phosphite. This simple exchange of carbonyl for the ligand L may be accomplished in acceptable yields (60–80%) using uv irradiation (Jaouen and Dabard, 1974a). The electronic modifications thus realized are illustrated in Table III, which contains polarographic reduction data for diverse acetophenone derivatives.

TABLE III

Compounds	$E_{1/2}$ Volt (SCE); pH = 4.10
$C_6H_5COCH_3$	− 1.32
$(C_6H_5COCH_3)Cr(CO)_2P(O\phi)_3$	− 1.17
$(C_6H_5COCH_3)Cr(CO)_3$	− 1.07
$(C_6H_5COCH_3)Cr(CO)_2CS$	− 1.02

It has been shown that the pK_a of the acid $(C_6H_5CO_2H)Cr(CO)_2PPh_3$ (6.15) is greater than that of benzoic acid (5.68). These organometallic species of the type $Cr(CO)_2L$ may thus be placed in the following order of decreasing electron-attracting character:

$$Cr(CO)_2CS > Cr(CO)_3 > Cr(CO)_2P(O\phi)_3 > Cr(CO)_2P\phi_3$$

These distinctly different effects may be used either to increase the reactivity of, to augment the selectivity of, or to protect a complexed ligand. Thus, like free methyl phenylacetate, the complex $(C_6H_5CH_2CO_2CH_3)$-$Cr(CO)_2PPh_3$ is inert at 25° in DMF in the presence of an excess of NaH and CH_3I. However, if $(C_6H_5CO_2CH_2CH_3)Cr(CO)_2P(OPh)_3$ is reacted under the same conditions, the monoalkylated complex $[C_6H_5CH(CH_3)$-$CO_2CH_3]Cr(CO)_2P(OPh)_3$ is isolated (70% yield), together with a small amount of the disubstituted complex which may be separated by chromatography. If the complex $(C_6H_5CH_2CH_3)Cr(CO)_2CS$ is reacted with CH_3I/t-BuOK in DMSO for 1 hr at 25°, the methylated complex $[C_6H_5C$-$(CH_3)_3]Cr(CO)_2CS$ is obtained (55% yield). Decomplexation of the products may be accomplished using the methods described for the chromium tricarbonyl derivatives although chromatographic purification is now necessary.

The alkylation of the complex $BCTCH_2CH_2CO_2CH_3$ **(XXI)** presents an interesting problem because of the presence of two possible reaction sites in the molecule, i.e., either α to the complexed ring or α to the ester function. In fact, methylation (25°, DMF, NaH/CH_3I, 9 hr) is regiospecific at the carbon atom β to the complexed ring; the monosubstituted complex $[C_6H_5CH_2$-$CH(CH_3)CO_2CH_3]Cr(CO)_3$ **(XXII)** is isolated in 65% yield, together with 10% of the disubstituted complex **(XXIII)**.

$L = CO, CS$

(XXI)

(XXII)

(XXIII)

If a more strongly attracting group such as $Cr(CO)_2CS$ is complexed to the ring, the reaction is surprisingly still regiospecific in the same way, but only the disubstituted complex is obtained after the same reaction period. This β-activation of the arene may be the result of carbanion stabilization by either the metal or the aromatic ring, or may be due to steric factors.

Among the reactions utilizing the property of the $Cr(CO)_3$ group to stabilize α-carbonium ions are the facile reductions of ester, ketone, and alcohol functions bonded to complexed rings using $AlCl_3/LiAlH_4$ in hydrocarbon solvents (Dabard et al., 1969; Dabard and Jaouen, 1969). It has previously been recognized that the ease of this reduction may be related to the extent of carbonium ion stabilization (Nystrom, 1955; Nystrom and Berger, 1958; Brown and White, 1957; Schlögl et al., 1961). The reaction is facilitated if the $Cr(CO)_3$ group is replaced by a stronger donor such as $Cr(CO)_2PPh_3$; in this case, the yields are practically quantitative (Jaouen and Dabard, 1974a). Synthetic applications of this extraordinary stabilization will very likely be the subject of much research in the future, particularly since Seyferth and Eschbach (1975) succeeded in isolating a stable carbonium ion in the benchrotrene series.

VI. REACTIVITY OF AN AROMATIC MOIETY COMPLEXED BY $Cr(CO)_3$

The increase in the value of the nmr coupling constant $J(^{13}C—H)$ (Emanuel and Randall, 1969) between the carbon and hydrogen atoms of an arene ring complexed by $Cr(CO)_3$ indicates an increase in the effective electronegativity of the ring carbon atoms (Khandkarova et al., 1970). The chemical reactivity of the aromatic skeleton must therefore be profoundly altered by complexation. Thus, e.g., the benchrotrene protons undergo isotopic exchange, either acid or base catalyzed (Kursanov et al., 1970, 1972; Ashraf, 1972), under conditions where the free ligands do not react. (Chlorobenzene)chromium tricarbonyl undergoes a rapid nucleophilic substitution reaction with methoxide ion to give (anisole)chromium tricarbonyl (Nicholls and Whiting, 1959). This substitution reaction has been extended to other cases; in particular, it has permitted the establishment of the absolute configuration of a great number of chiral complexes by correlation with optically active o- and m-fluorobenchrotrene esters (Jaouen and Dabard, 1970) and has allowed the preparation of cyano complexes previously unknown in the benchrotrene series (Jaouen et al., 1972). Kinetic aspects of this type of reaction have also been the subject of study (Brown and Raju, 1966; Tchissambou et al., 1972), especially with respect to the action of amines on fluorobenchrotrene (Bunnett and Hermann, 1971). This last reaction is base catalyzed; in the $Cr(CO)_3$ complexes the slow step in the reaction is the elimination of fluoride from the intermediate, while in the noncomplexed ligand (e.g., p-nitrofluorobenzene), the rate limiting factor is initial nucleophilic attack. To a certain extent this accents the differences between the free and complexed systems and, moreover, is in accord with the postulate of both exo amine attack on the $Cr(CO)_3$ complex and a critical steric factor influencing the elimination of fluoride.

While theory predicts a slight difference in behavior of free and complexed arenes with respect to electrophilic attack (Saillard *et al.*, 1974), few studies have been devoted to this problem. Several groups (Ercoli *et al.*, 1959; Herberich and Fischer, 1962) have, however, succeeded in acetylating derivatives of (benzene)chromium tricarbonyl using mild conditions, but in poor yields. These poor yields probably result from the presence of "free" $AlCl_3$, which causes rupture of the metal–ring bond, rather than from inertness of the complex to electrophilic attack. The steric bulkiness of the $Cr(CO)_3$ group may also be involved in the reduced reactivity of the complexed rings toward electrophilic reagents. Nevertheless an increase in the percentage of "ortho" isomers (by comparison with the free ligand) has been obtained (Jackson and Jennings, 1969; Dabard and Jaouen, 1974). This increase has been interpreted in terms of a phenonium ion intermediate containing a 1,3-dienoid system, the distribution of whose orbitals is more compatible with the chromium ligand bond; the intermediate then yields the ortho complex. This change in isomer distribution is not great enough, however, to be useful in organic synthesis.

VII. PHENYLATION OF NUCLEOPHILES VIA NEUTRAL ORGANOMETALLIC INTERMEDIATES

A. Temporary Activation of an Aromatic Species by the $Cr(CO)_3$ Group

The work previously described concerning the activation to nucleophiles of aromatic species complexed by $Cr(CO)_3$ has led Semmelhack *et al.* (1975; Semmelhack and Hall, 1974a,b) to a study of the synthetic implications of the phenylation of carbanions via benchrotrene complexes. The introduction and then displacement of activating groups are problems which are not easily solved in organic chemistry. Thus, methods involving nucleophilic addition are rarely used for the fixation of carbon substituents in the synthesis of aromatic natural products (although an approach using a benzyne intermediate has been reported) (Julia *et al.*, 1969). There are, however, several cases [e.g., the synthesis of lysergic acid (Julia *et al.*, 1969) and of cephalotaxin (Semmelhack *et al.*, 1972a)] where the desired product might be obtained directly by combination of a stabilized carbanion with an aromatic moiety. The ease of complexation and displacement of the $Cr(CO)_3$ group thus makes it the reagent of choice in such syntheses.

Scheme I outlines such an approach and represents a very simple case, i.e., the reaction of the anion of isobutyronitrile **(XXIV)** with chlorobenchrotrene **(XXV)** (25°, 20 hr) to give the alkylbenchrotrene **(XXVI)** in 95%

purity (78% yield). Cleavage of the organometallic intermediate is quantitative using iodine in ether at 0°.

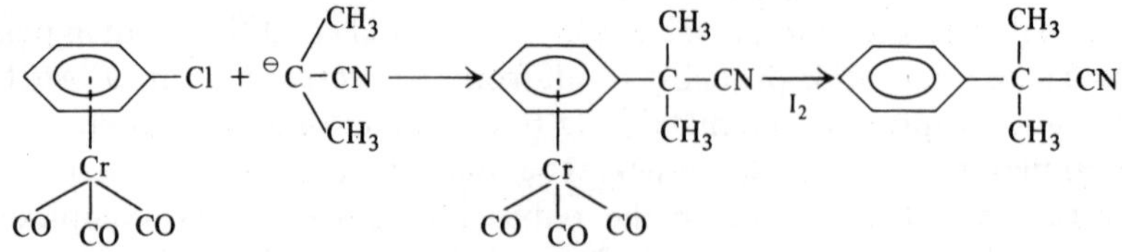

(XXV) (XXIV) (XXVI) (XXVII)

Scheme 1

The results of several other reactions are listed in Table IV.

TABLE IV

Anion	Product	Yield
$^{\ominus}C(CH_3)_2CN$	$\phi - C(CH_3)_2CN$	85-90
$^{\ominus}C(CH_3)_2CO_2Et$	$\phi - C(CH_3)_2CO_2Et$	71
$^{\ominus}C(CH_3)_2CO_2^-$	$\phi - C(CH_3)_2CO_2H$	63
$^{\ominus}CH(CO_2Et)_2$	$\phi - CH(CO_2Et)_2$	51
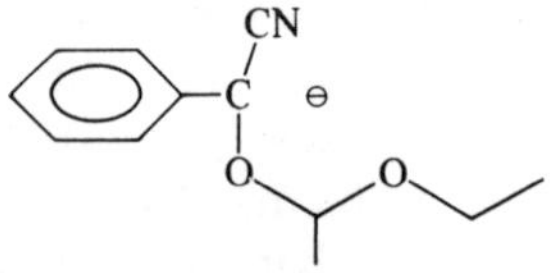	$\phi - CO - \phi$	88
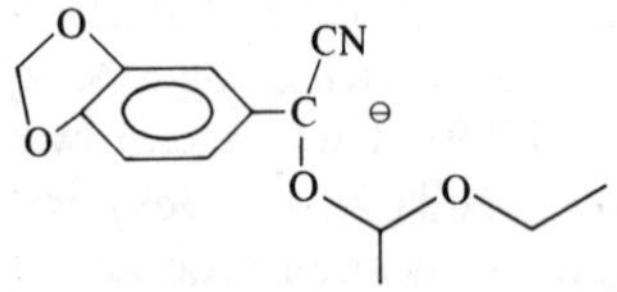	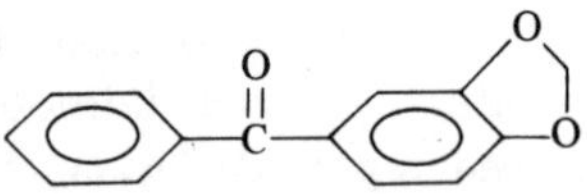	90

It may be noted that reactions involving secondary or primary anions, such as the lithium salts of acetophenone, acetonitrile, or *tert*-butylacetate, are less efficient. The explanation probably lies in a competing side reaction at the hydrogens α to the ring, which are rendered acidic by complexation.

A change in the halogen may be used to ameliorate some of the inconveniences of the above reaction. It has already been verified that the dependence on reactivity as a function of the leaving group is the same for the halogeno–benchrotrene series as it is for classical aromatic nucleophilic substitution reactions (Bunnett, 1958). This is illustrated in Table V for the reaction of complexes with sodium diethylmalonate.

TABLE V

Complex	Entry	Conditions	Phenylmalonate yield, %
(XXV)	1	25°, 48 hr	5
	2	50°, 24 hr	51
	3	25°, 48 hr	0
(XXVIII)	4	25°, 48 hr	63
	5	50°, 0.5 hr	72
	6	50°, 20 hr	>95

The greater reactivity of the fluoro complex, already evaluated using kinetic measurements (Brown and Raju, 1966), thus leads to yields much superior to those obtained by the action of sodium diethylmalonate on chlorobenchrotrene **(XXV)**. Furthermore, the reaction below, opposite to that which occurs with the chloro complex **(XXV)**, may be carried out in a yield of 94% (after oxidation).

(XXVIII)   (XXIX)   (XXX)

A plausible mechanism for this carbanion phenylation reaction is the following:

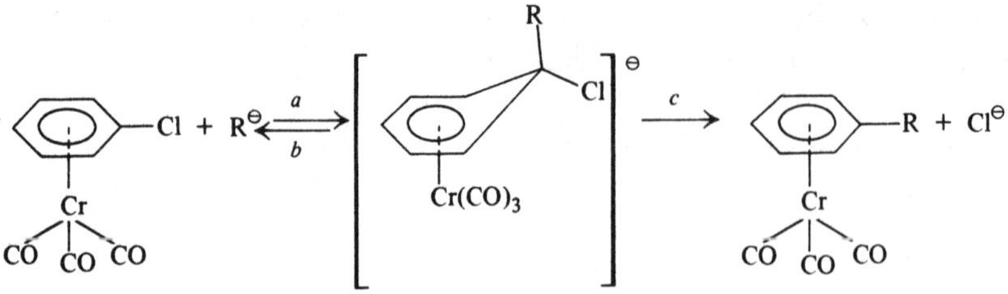

Scheme 2

Attack of the carbanion to form the π-(alkylcyclohexadienyl)chromium tricarbonyl anion **(XXXI)** may be postulated, followed by irreversible loss of the halogen anion. This mechanism is based particularly on arguments drawn from an analogy both with the mechanism of classical aromatic nucleophilic substitution (Bunnett, 1958; Sauer and Visgen, 1960; Ross, 1963) and with anionic attack on cationic complexes of iron (Helling and Braitsch, 1970) and manganese (Walker and Mawby, 1971, 1973a,b). In fact, in these latter cases, structures similar to **XXXI** may be isolated.

However, if the reaction is followed by nmr and stopped after a low degree of conversion, one is led to the conclusion that the actual mechanism is more complicated than that outlined in Scheme 2.

In fact, it has been shown that:

1. Steps *a* and *b* are very rapid compared to step *c*.

2. Attack may occur at several positions (ortho or meta) relative to the halogen substituent. This is consistent with the previously unexplained partial racemization observed during nucleophilic attack on optically active fluoro complexes (Jaouen and Dabard, 1970).

3. Proton addition to the intermediate complex may lead to dihydrobenzene derivatives.

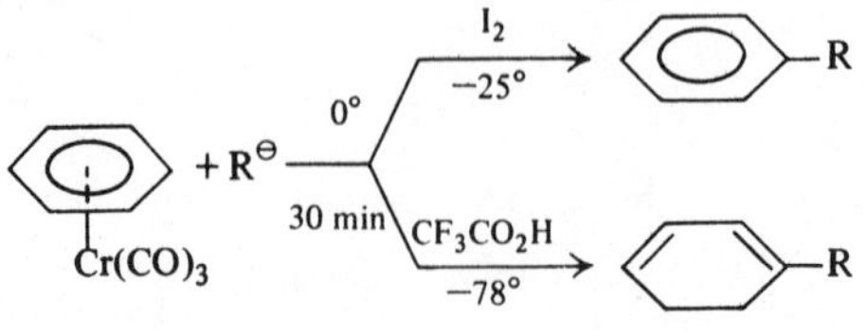

This last fact, coupled with the observation that significant quantities of benchrotrene itself are present in the reaction medium (and thus susceptible to nucleophilic attack) has led to the synthesis of substituted arenes and cyclohexadienes from (benzene)chromium tricarbonyl. Some results are listed in Table VI (Semmelhack *et al.*, 1975, 1976).

TABLE VI

Entry	Carbanion	Product	Yield, %
1	$LiC(CH_3)_2CN$	$\phi C(CH_3)_2CN$	94
2	$LiCH_2CN$	ϕCH_2CN	68
3	$Li-\langle\!\!\begin{smallmatrix}S-\\S-\end{smallmatrix}\!\!\rangle$	$\phi-\langle\!\!\begin{smallmatrix}S-\\S-\end{smallmatrix}\!\!\rangle$	93
4	$Li-\overset{CN}{\underset{O\frown O\frown}{CH}}CH_2CH_3$	$\phi-\overset{O}{\overset{\|}{C}}CH_2CH_2CH_3$	90
5	$Li-\overset{CN}{\underset{O\frown O\frown}{CH(CH_3)_2}}$	$\phi-\overset{O}{\overset{\|}{C}}-CH(CH_3)_2$	88
6	$LiC(CH_3)_3$	$\phi-C(CH_3)_3$	97
7	$Li-C_6H_4-CH_3$	$\phi-C_6H_4-CH_3$	71
8	$KC(CH_3)_2CO_2tBu$	$\phi-C(CH_3)_2CO_2tBu$	88
9	$LiCH_2CO_2tBu$	$\phi-CH_2CO_2tBu$	87
10	$LiCH(CH_3)CO_2tBu$	$\phi-CH(CH_3)CO_2\,tBu$	88

Predominant or exclusive formation of meta-substituted aromatics occurs by carbanion attack on (toluene)- or (anisole)chromium tricarbonyl (Semmelhack and Clark, 1977). The direct alkylation of (ethylbenzene)chromium tricarbonyl has been reported by Card and Trahanovsky (1973).

$o:m:p$
$1:97:2$ (86% total yield)

This new method of carbanion phenylation would seem to be quite useful, since only mild conditions (0°) are necessary, and recently a much improved synthetic method for benchrotrene has been reported (Rausch, 1974). It may

be noted that, contrary to the halogeno–benchrotrene complexes, it is possible to utilize the enolates of primary and secondary esters (Table VI,
entries 9 and 10). However, reaction with ketone enolates again fails, even
if potassium is used as the cation instead of lithium, or HMPA is used as
solvent in place of THF in an attempt to displace the equilibrium in the
first step of Scheme 2.

B. Other Methods of Activation

At least in certain cases, such as acetophenone, the problem described
above may be solved by using another procedure for formal nucleophilic
substitution (Semmelhack et al., 1973). This procedure is based on the observation that aryl and vinyl halides are greatly activated by oxidative addition
to transition metals in low oxidation states (Semmelhack et al., 1971,
1972b).* A simple example is described in the following scheme:

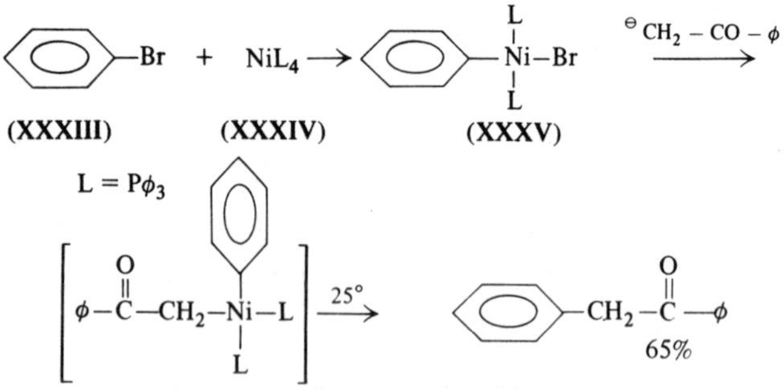

Prior preparation of the phenyl nickel complex (XXXV) is not necessary;
the desired product may be obtained by simply stirring bromobenzene (XXXIII) (or iodobenzene), tetrakis(triphenylphosphine)nickel(O)
(XXXIV), and the sodium salt of acetophenone at −78°. From a consideration of the scheme, a catalytic effect by the nickel may be expected. Although
this effect does exist, it has a poor efficiency; thus, starting from 0.14 molar
equivalents of the nickel complex (XXXV), a 250% yield of the phenylbenzyl
ketone (XXXVII) may be obtained based on the nickel catalyst.

The studies on the use of aryl nickel complexes for novel syntheses of
heterocyclic compounds have also been extensively developed. Miller et al.

* Limitations because of coupling reactions in the cases of Grignard and lithium reagents,
and in the case of the Ullmann reaction using metallic copper, are described in Semmelhack et
al. (1971).

(1968) reported the conversion of *trans*-chloro(2-alkylphenyl)bis(triethyl-phosphine)nickel(II) (XXXVIII) into indene (XL) (yields 58%) on heating in tetrachloroethylene (XXXIX) at 85°–90°. XXXVIII is prepared in high yields from *trans*-dichlorobis(triethylphoshine)nickel(II) and 2-alkylphenyl magnesium chloride. Compound XXXVIII is of interest because the benzylic hydrogen and the olefinic bond are potential reactants with the transition metal at an apical site in the planar complex.

(XXXVIII) (XXXIX) (XL) (XLI)

In an extension of these studies, a new synthesis of indole derivatives was reported (Mori and Ban, 1976a) from 2-chloro-N-methyl-N-allylaniline (XLII) by refluxing in ether for several hours with tetrakis(triphenyl-phosphine)nickel [Ni(PPh$_3$)$_4$]. The latter was prepared *in situ* to prevent deallylation. After oxygen was bubbled through the solution to convert PPh$_3$ into O ← PPh$_3$ for easy handling, the 1,3-dimethyl indole (XLIII) was obtained in a yield of 45.6%.

(XLII) (XLIII)

This reaction can be utilized for the synthesis of various indole derivatives and adaptations of this method have been applied to new syntheses in oxindole series (Mori and Ban, 1976b).

VIII. ELECTROPHILIC REACTIVITY OF CATIONIC ARENE COMPLEXES

It is known that nucleophilic substitution of aromatic substrates may be accomplished under photochemical conditions (Rossi and Bunnett, 1973; Wurbels and Letsinger, 1974; Cornelisse and Havinga, 1975). In this respect, the preceding results are consistent with the hypothesis by Ugo that metal coordination of unsaturated molecules is equivalent to their photochemical excitation (Ugo, 1973). When one is dealing with organometallic ions, this activation may be more apparent as a result of the presence of a formal charge, and a variety of synthetic applications may be envisaged as a result of the diversity of ionic complexes available. The electrophilic character of certain organometallic cations such as $[C_6H_7Fe(CO)_3]^+$ and $[C_7H_7Cr(CO)_3]^+$ is now well documented, and their use in synthesis has been recently explored (Birch and Jenkins, 1975; Birch et al., 1975; Kane-Maguire et al., 1973, 1974, 1975; Hackett and Jaouen, 1975).

The susceptibility of arenes coordinated to metallic ions toward nucleophilic attack by H^- or R^- (R = alkyl or aryl) is well known (Jones and Wilkinson, 1964; Fischer and Schmidt, 1967). In an early report, Nesmeyanov compared the lability of the aromatic halogen substituent of the (chlorobenzene)(cyclopentadienyl)iron cation (LXIV) with that found for $ClC_6H_5Cr(CO)_3$ (XXV) (Nesmeyanov et al., 1967). The following reaction occurs under mild conditions (30°–60°, 20–30 min).

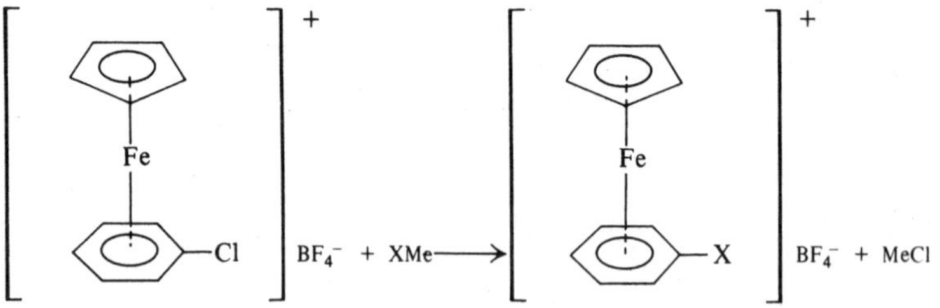

(XLIV)   (XLV)

$X = C_2H_5O^-, C_6H_5O^-, C_6H_5S^-, n - C_4H_9S^-, C_6H_4\underset{CO}{\overset{CO}{\diagdown\diagup}}N^-$
Me = Na, K

η^6-Arene-η^5-cyclopentadienyliron cation complexes of structural type XLIV can be synthesized by a ligand exchange reaction between ferrocene and simple arenes in the presence of aluminum powder and aluminum chloride (Sutherland, 1977). For polynuclear aromatic hydrocarbons, stereospecific hydrogenation occurs during the ligand exchange process (Sutherland et al., 1975). For example, 9,10-dimethylanthracene reacts with ferrocene, $AlCl_3$, and Al to give the η^6-cis-(endo-9,10-dihydro)-9,10-dimethylanthracene-η^5-cyclopentadienyliron cation, from which cis-9,10-dihydro-9,10-dimethylanthracene can be obtained by pyrolysis of photolysis (Sutherland et al., 1977). This reaction sequence is the most efficient route to cis-9,10-dihydro-9,10-dimethylanthracene.

With charged organometallic complexes, two problems often arise: that of the site of attack and that of the nature of the leaving group in the adduct so formed. In fact, depending on the nature of the nucleophile (e.g., the degree of hardness or softness), the nature of the metal, the total charge on the ion, the kind of ligands, and even the solvent, attack may occur at the arene ligand, at another ligand, or at the metal center, and displacement of a ligand may or may not result (Block et al., 1976; Casey and Bunnell, 1976). Examples of all these possibilities are known, and sometimes the orientation of attack may be altered by only a subtle change in one of these factors (Hackett and Jaouen, 1975; Sweigart et al., 1976). An explanation for these differences in behavior remains to be found, but an understanding may allow selective orientation of nucleophilic attack toward a desired site. On the other hand, when an arene cation is reacted with a charged nucleophile, a neutral cyclohexadienyl complex is often obtained, and a question then arises regarding the nature of the leaving group when the aromatic planar structure is recreated, for example, by decomplexation.

The example of cyanocyclohexadienyl manganese tricarbonyl will serve to illustrate these points. Arene complexes of the type $(C_6H_{6-n}Me_n)Mn(CO)_3^+$ (**XLVI**) react with cyanide ion under mild conditions (ambient temperature) to give the exo-cyanocyclohexadienyl complexes $(C_6H_{6-n}Me_nCN)Mn(CO)_3$ (**XLVII**) as the kinetic products, in which the cyano group is attached to a nonsubstituted carbon atom (Walker and Mawby, 1973b). The hexamethyl-benzene complex reacts differently to form the $(C_6Me_6)Mn(CO)_2CN$ complex. Compounds of this type have previously been obtained starting from $(C_6H_{6-n}Me_n)Mn(CO)_2I$ or by decomposition of cyanocyclohexa-dienyl complexes in water or methanol. Despite the labile character of the exo cyano group, these complexes may be used as novel intermediates in the synthesis of cyano arenes. Several attempts at selective abstraction of the endo hydrogen under mild conditions have failed;* however, oxidation of the products with ceric sulphate in sulphuric acid liberates the cyano arenes, uncontaminated by benzene or mesitylene, in yields of 73–80%.

(XLVI)   (XLVII)

Besides H^-, D^-, Me^-, and Ph^-, other nucleophiles such as N_3^-, NCO^- and the anions of diethyl malonate and pentane-2,4-dionate (Walker and Mawby, 1973b) also react with $(C_6H_{6-n}Me_n)Mn(CO)_3^+$.

In a comparative study, the reaction of nucleophiles with the analogous series of complex cations $(C_6H_nMe_{6-n}; n = 0, 2)$ $Cr(CO)_2NO^+$ was examined. In this case, only exo attack of H^-, D^-, and Me^- was observed (Connelly and Kelly, 1974). For reasons which are unclear, the reactivity of these chromium complexes with respect to nucleophilic attack is less than that of the manganese complexes. In any case, this alteration introduced by the cationic NO^+ ligand does not produce any synthetic advantages over those obtained with a simple $Cr(CO)_3$ group.

Pauson and Segal (1975) have recently prepared tricarbonyl (η-halogeno-benzene) manganese salts. The high reactivity of the manganese complexes is utilized in the preparation of other functionally substituted arene complexes by substitution of the chlorine atom with anionic $(MeO^-, PhO^-, PhS^-,$ and $N_3^-)$ or amine (ammonia, aniline, n-butylamine, piperidine, dimethylamine, diethylamine, and N-methylaniline) nucleophiles. The expected substitution complexes have been obtained in good to excellent yields. Displacement of the substituted arene from complexes was demonstrated on heating the N-diethylamine complex in acetonitrile, resulting in complete conversion into the tris(acetonitrile) cation $[Mn(CO)_3(NCMe)_3]^+$ within 15 min. This makes the manganese complexes attractive intermediates, perhaps even better than benchrotrene complexes, for facilitating nucleophilic substitution of halogenoarenes, particularly with sensitive or expensive nucleophiles.

---

* Several rare examples of such abstractions using triphenylmethyl tetrafluoroborate (Khand et al., 1969) and N-bromosuccinimide (Efraty and Maitlis, 1967) are known.

In a similar manner, certain bis(arene)iron(II) salts react easily with nucleophiles and may be used in organic synthesis. For example, $(mesitylene)_2Fe(PF_6)_2$ reacts with phenyl, *tert*-butyl, and vinyllithium to give either the compound **XLVIII** or the pseudo-ferrocene derivative **XLIX**, according to the stoichiometry of the reaction (Helling and Braitsch, 1970).

(**XLVIIIa**): R = C_6H_5
(**XLVIIIb**): R = $t - $ Bu
(**XLVIIIc**): R = C_2H_3

(**XLIXa**): R = C_6H_5
(**XLIXb**): R = $t - C_4H_9$
(**XLIXc**): R = C_2H_3

Decomplexation occurs with loss of hydrogen; the total synthesis thus consists of nucleophilic substitution via an iron intermediate of hydrogen in an electron-rich aromatic nucleus by aryl or alkyl groups. Thermal decomplexation of **XLVIIIa** at 216° gives an equimolar mixture of mesitylene and phenylmesitylene. Oxidation of **XLIXa** with $KMnO_4$ gives a 95% yield of phenylmesitylene. This method appears to be the best available for the synthesis of phenylmesitylene, since the overall yield of 35% with all steps included is much greater than the yield obtained using methyl magnesium bromide, bromobenzene, and $CoCl_2$, which is not much greater than 15% (Castro *et al.*, 1958). Similarly, oxidation of **XLIXc** with ceric ammonium nitrate provides an 82% yield of vinylmesitylene (overall yield based on mesitylene = 27%).

Thermal decomposition of **XLVIIIb** at 233° yields mesitylene without a trace of *tert*-butylmesitylene. However, oxidation of **XLIXb** with $KMnO_4$ gives an 18% yield of *tert*-butylmesitylene, in addition to mesitylene (overall yield = 9%, compared to 3% by the only other known route via organo-magnesium reagents) (Burgstahler *et al.*, 1965). Several other extensions, with varying degrees of success, of this reaction have been reported (Helling and Cash, 1974).

Several other carbon nucleophiles bearing various functional groups (CN,

CH_2CO_2, $CHCH_3NO_2$, CH_2COOt-C_4H_9) also undergo easy addition to mesitylene coordinated to Fe(II), but only monoadducts are observed. Oxidation of these compounds with ceric ammonium nitrate gives 1 : 1 mixtures of mesitylene and the substituted mesitylene. The yields of the latter, based on the products isolated, are of the order of 50%.

On the other hand, with oxygen and nitrogen nucleophiles ($LiNH_2$, $LiN(CH_3)_2$, $NaN[Si(CH_3)_3]_2$, $LiOCH_3$, KOt-butyl), the product obtained (L) results from proton abstraction from a methyl group of the methylated arene coordinated to iron. Similar activation of the protons of α-methyl groups with respect to basic attack has been found in complexes of duroquinone (M = Co, Rh, Ir) (Slocum and Engelmann, 1972) and in pentamethylcyclopentadienyl (M = Rh) complexes (Kang and Maitlis, 1971), as well as in the benchrotrene series (Jaouen et al., 1975).

(L)

IX. STEREOCHEMICAL CONSEQUENCES OF THE TRANSITION METAL COMPLEXATION OF AN ARENE

It has previously been stated that attack by nucleophiles on cationic arene rings occurs stereospecifically in an exo fashion. In fact, coordination by a transition metal confers a third dimension on the molecule which has several stereochemical consequences. For example, electrophilic or nucleophilic attack at the reactive center of an alicyclic ring ortho-condensed to an aromatic moiety always occurs stereospecifically in an exo fashion. Arene derivatives containing different ortho or meta substitutents are chiral, and numerous examples exist of the resolution of benchrotrene derivatives into optical isomers (Mandelbaum *et al.*, 1963; Falk *et al.*, 1966; Dabard and Meyer, 1967; Dabard *et al.*, 1969; Jaouen *et al.*, 1972a).

Stereospecificity has been observed in the metal hydride reduction of a carbonyl group situated α to a complexed ring, but included in a rigid structure [e.g., indanone **(LI)**]. Whatever the reducing agent used, only the endo isomer **LII** is obtained.

(LI)   (LII)

This total stereospecificity has been interpreted in several ways. Jackson *et al.* (1969) attribute this essentially to steric control by the Cr(CO)₃ group to the direction of attack. These conclusions are based on the fact that the reduction of (2-tetralone)chromium tricarbonyl, in which the carbonyl is more remote from the Cr(CO)₃ group, leads to 5–7% of the exo alcohol. At the same time, this result may also be interpreted in terms of a partial electronic control of the direction of attack, for remoteness of the carbonyl to the 2 position may diminish the electronic influence of the $Cr(CO)_3$ group. The large dipole moment of the $Cr(CO)_3$ group (5D) (Fischer and Schreiner, 1959) seems to favor an electronic control of attack being at least as important as steric control. In support of this postulate, the reduction of (2-*tert*-butyl-1-indanone)chromium tricarbonyl (Jaouen *et al.*, 1972b) is equally stereospecific, although an examination of molecular models indicates that the *tert*-butyl group should have a greater steric influence on the ketone function than the $Cr(CO)_3$ group.

The same argument holds for electrophilic attack of a carbanion created α to the indane carbonyl **(LIII)**:

(LI)   (LIII)

These properties have been used in the synthesis of derivatives of indanone and tetralone, with the aim of obtaining compounds of known configuration, both in a racemic and an optically active series.

A. Synthesis of Indanols

No common route of access exists for the synthesis of cis and trans alkyl indanols. According to literature reports, reduction of certain of these ketones by metallic hydrides leads to mixtures whose composition has not always been determined accurately. However, it is now stereospecific for indanones regardless of the nature or position of the substituent bonded to the alicyclic ring (Jaouen et al., 1972). The indanols obtained always have the alcohol function in a position cis to the $Cr(CO)_3$ group. Thus, decomplexation leads quantitatively to indanols of well defined configuration. Caro and Jaouen (1974) have applied this procedure to the synthesis of several indanols substituted in the 2 or 3 position by various alkyl groups. The precursor (indanone)chromium tricarbonyl is prepared either by cyclization of the corresponding propionic acid derivative (LIV), or by direct complexation (LV) (Jaouen and Dabard, 1974b). Separation of the two stereoisomers (LVI and LIX) is followed by reduction with KBH_4. The pure cis (LXI) or trans (LVIII) indanols may be recovered after decomplexation. Scheme 3 summarizes these different steps for the synthesis of the 2-alkyl-substituted indanols. The method leads to overall yields of the order of 60%. These syntheses have been applied to the following systems:

$$R_1 = CH_3, C_2H_5, CH(CH_3)_2 \text{ with } R_2 = R_3 = R_4 = H$$
$$R_2 = CH_3, C_2H_5, CH(CH_3)_2 \text{ with } R_1 = R_3 = R_4 = H$$
$$R_3 = CH_3, C_2H_5, CH(CH_3)_2, C(CH_3)_3 \text{ with } R_1 = R_2 = R_4 = H$$
$$R_4 = CH_3, C_2H_5, CH(CH_3)_2, C(CH_3)_3 \text{ with } R_1 = R_2 = R_3 = H$$

The preceding methods may be applied not only to the synthesis of racemic indanols, but also to the synthesis of optically active indanols having an optical purity of 100%. The first example reported in the literature concerned the preparation of optically pure 3-methyl-1-indanols (LXII, LXIII) (Scheme 4) (Jaouen and Dabard, 1971).

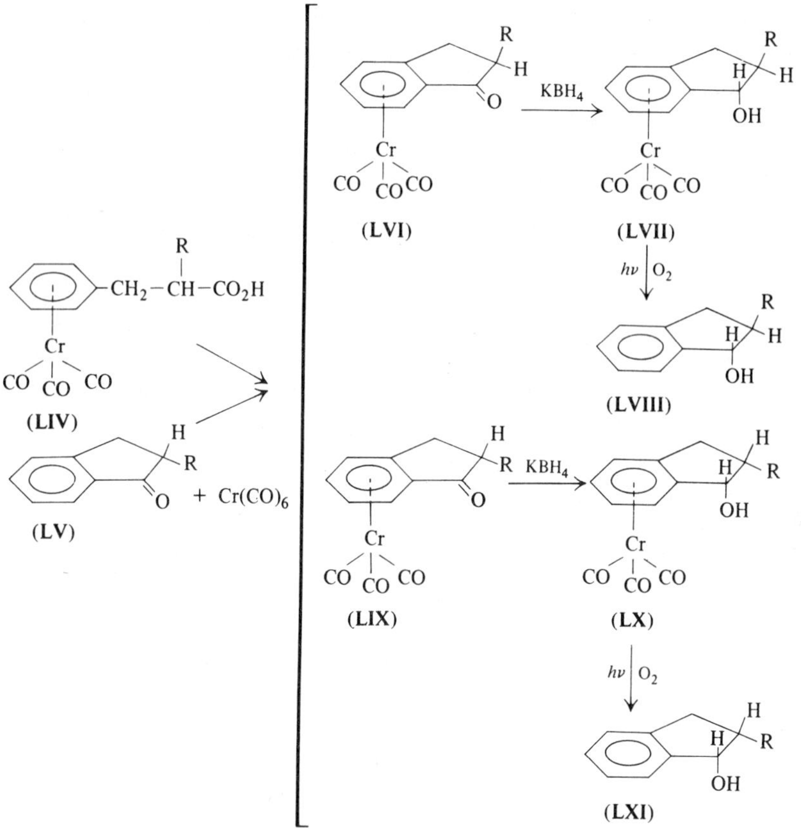

Scheme 3

B. Access to Optically Active Indanones and Tetralones

Another route to optically active 2-alkyl indanones has recently been developed (Jaouen and Meyer, 1975) and has been extended to 2-alkyl tetralones.

The stereospecificity of electrophilic attack of a carbanion created α to the ketonic group of the (indanone)- or (tetralone)chromium tricarbonyl is again utilized. However, the difficulty in these syntheses resides essentially in the access to optically active (indanone)- or (tetralone)chromium tricar-

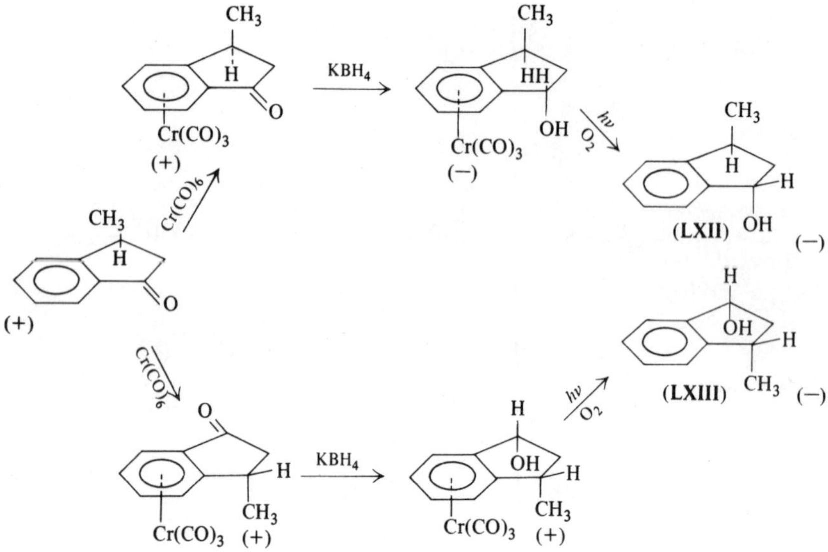

Scheme 4

bonyl complexes. This difficulty may be overcome by resolution of the acid succinate of (indanol)chromium tricarbonyl, followed by hydrolysis and oxidation (Scheme 5).

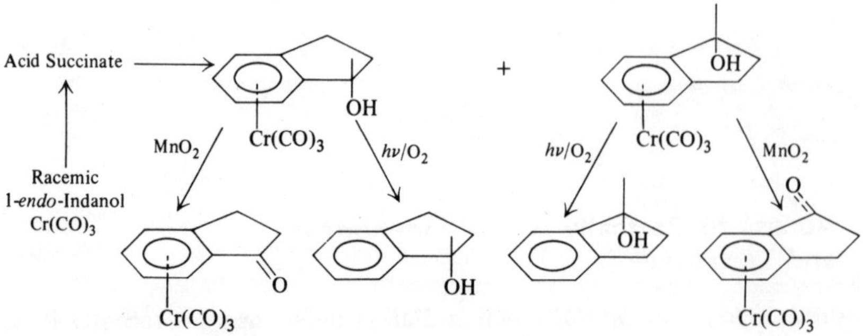

Scheme 5

Access to the optically pure (indanone)chromium tricarbonyl is thus achieved via the optically pure indanol. An identical procedure may be used to obtain (tetralone)chromium tricarbonyl from the optically active tetralol.

Methylation of (indanone)chromium tricarbonyl **(LI)** using CH_3I/NaH may be carried out in DMF/benzene to give (2-methylindanone)chromium tricarbonyl **(LXIV)**.

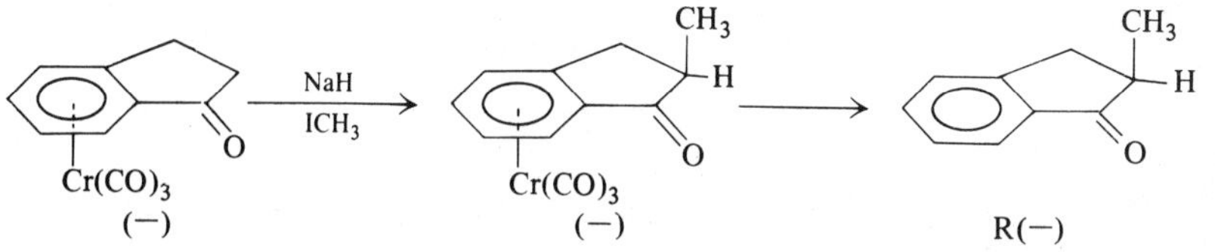

$$\underset{\text{(LI)}}{(-)} \qquad \underset{\text{(LXIV)}}{(-)} \qquad \underset{\text{(LXV)}}{R(-)}$$

Despite a basic medium favoring an exo–endo equilibration of the ketones, only the exo derivative **(LXIV)** is observed. However, in the presence of excess methylating agent, formation of the dimethylated derivative occurs. Decomplexation gives 2-methylindanone **(LXV)** having an optical purity of 100%.

Another example of the total control of stereochemistry by the $Cr(CO)_3$ group during the creation of an asymmetric center α to the ketonic carbonyl is shown in Scheme 6.

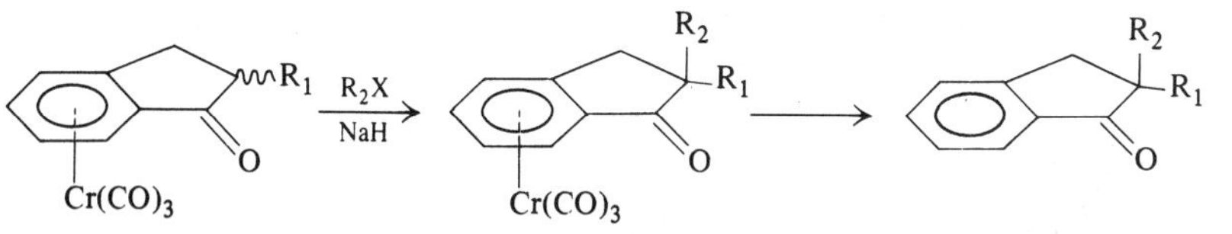

$$\text{(LXVI)} \qquad \text{(LXVII)} \qquad \text{(LXVIII)}$$

Scheme 6

This general method has been applied in particular to the case where $R_1 = CH_3$ and $R_2 = CH_2C_6H_5$. Vast synthetic possibilities are thus available for the preparation in high yields of indanone and tetralone derivatives disubstituted in the 2 position. These arene complexes (e.g., **LXVII**) are also of considerable use in annulation reactions (Jaouen and Meyer, 1976) and in the synthesis of spiro compounds (Meyer *et al.*, 1977).

Finally, following the lines previously described, des Abbayes and Boudeville (1977) have used the great stereospecificity of carbanion attack to alkylate indane esters **(LXIX)** using NaH/DMF or by phase transfer catalysis (Scheme 7).

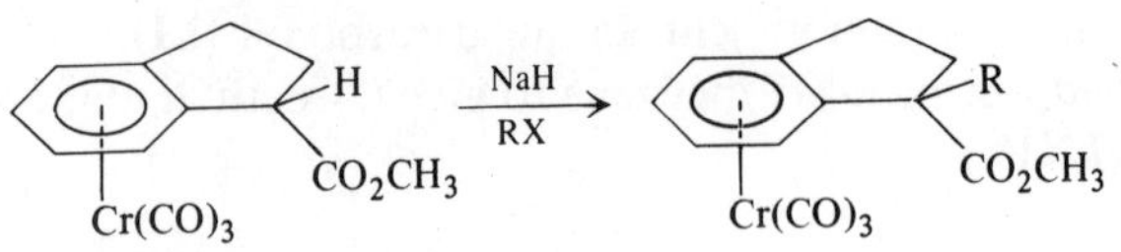

Scheme 7

C. Access to Optically Active Secondary and Tertiary Alcohols

Optically active alcohols are generally obtained by resolution of their acid phthalates, but the procedures are often complicated by dehydration or racemization (Ingersoll, 1944; Wilen, 1971; Boyle, 1971), particularly in the case of tertiary alcohols. These difficulties may be avoided by utilizing the stereospecificity observed in the addition of Grignard reagents.

1. Cyclic Series

Meyer and Jaouen (1974) have recently developed a general method for the resolution of the optical enantiomers of tertiary alcohols in the indanol and tetralol series. Optically active (indanone)- or (tetralone)chromium tricarbonyl (LXXI) is used as a starting material; attack of Grignard reagent is stereospecific and leads solely to the endo alcohol (LXXII) (Scheme 8).

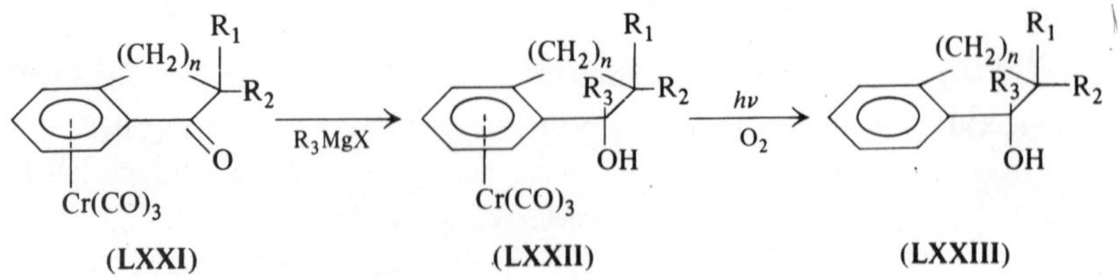

Scheme 8

2. Open Chain Series

Optically active secondary alcohols have been prepared by the highly stereoselective reduction of ketone complexes or by the addition of Grignard reagents to substituted benzaldehyde complexes (Meyer and Dabard, 1972). The complexed benzaldehydes (LXXIV) and aromatic ketones (LXXV) are obtained from the corresponding acids (Meyer, 1973). Reduction of the ketones (LXXV) with KBH_4 or reaction of the benzaldehyde complex (LXXIV) with the appropriate Grignard reagent leads to the same diastereoisomeric alcohols **(LXXVI, LXXVII)**, which are separable by chromatography. Finally, decomplexation yields the optically active alcohols having an optical purity of 100%.

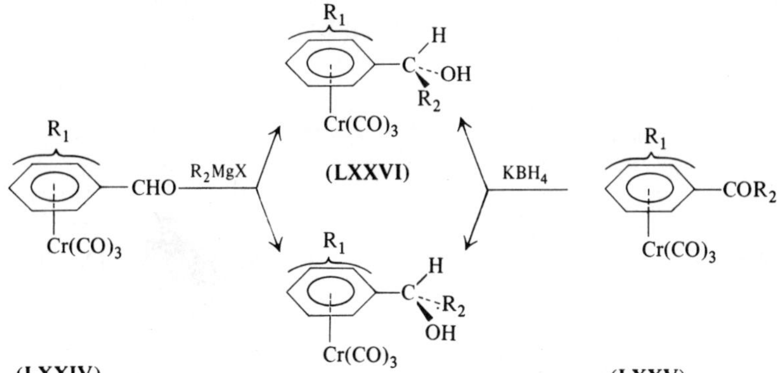

(LXXIV) (LXXVI) (LXXVII) (LXXV)

As an example, consider the reduction of (*o*-methylacetophenone)-chromium tricarbonyl **(LXXVIII)** outlined in Scheme 9 (Meyer *et al.*, 1971).

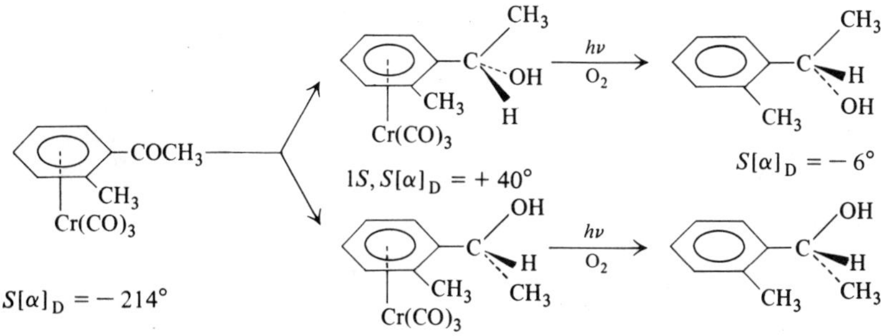

$1S[\alpha]_D = -214°$ (LXXVIII)

$1S, S[\alpha]_D = +40°$ $S[\alpha]_D = -6°$

$1S, R[\alpha]_D = +27°$ $R[\alpha]_D = +6°$

Scheme 9

D. Access to Deuterated Indanes

Utilizing both the activation of side chains bonded to an aromatic ring complexed by $Cr(CO)_3$, and the stereospecificity of electrophilic attack of carbanions created on these chains, Trahanovsky and Card (1972) have developed a synthesis of indane derivatives deuterated in well-defined positions, with isotopic purities greater than 96%.

The combined action of *t*-BuOK and DMSO-d_6 on complexed indane results in exclusive deuterium substitution of the two exo protons bonded to the carbons α to the ring. The stereospecificity of this substitution may clearly be demonstrated by reaction of the exo **(LXXXI)** and endo **(LXXIX)** derivatives of (1-methylindane)chromium tricarbonyl.

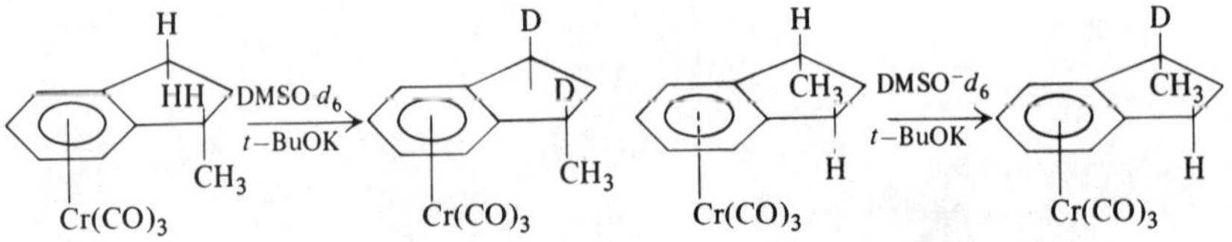

(LXXIX)   (LXXX)   (LXXXI)   (LXXXII)

E. General Access to Aromatic Glycols of Known Configuration

For a compound of such a simple constitution as bis(α-hydroxyethyl)-benzene, only one of the diastereoisomeric forms has been described, but not identified. Besançon *et al.* (1975) have developed a method which permits the preparation of these diastereoisomers via a chromium tricarbonyl intermediate.

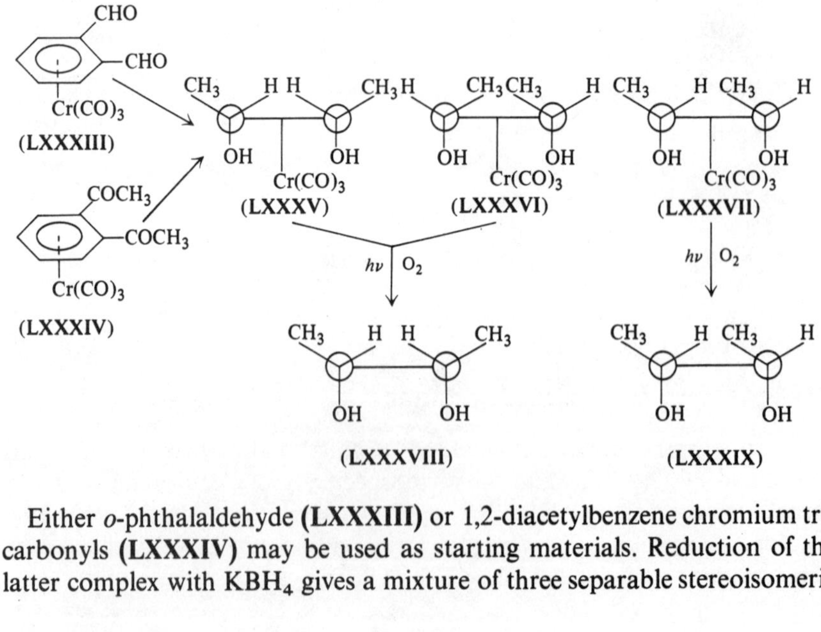

(LXXXIII)

(LXXXIV)

(LXXXV)   (LXXXVI)   (LXXXVII)

(LXXXVIII)   (LXXXIX)

Either *o*-phthalaldehyde **(LXXXIII)** or 1,2-diacetylbenzene chromium tricarbonyls **(LXXXIV)** may be used as starting materials. Reduction of the latter complex with KBH_4 gives a mixture of three separable stereoisomeric benchrotrene glycols: two meso pseudoasymmetric compounds (LXXXV, LXXXVI) and one racemic (LXXXVII).

Photochemical decomplexation of the two meso pseudoasymmetric benchrotrene stereoisomers yields the same meso benzene glycol (LXXX-VIII), while decomplexation of the racemic benchrotrene glycol (LXXXVII) yields a racemic benzene glycol (LXXXIX). The overall yield using this procedure is not particularly high, but it may be generalized to the synthesis of other aromatic glycols.

X. AROMATIZATION OF DIENE STRUCTURES VIA COMPLEXATION

The aromatization observed by Birch *et al.* (1965), involving loss of a molecule of methanol on condensation of 1-methoxycyclohexa-1,4-diene or its derivatives with $M(CO)_6$ (M = Cr, Mo, W), has been applied to the synthesis of 3-deoxy steroid hormones (Birch *et al.*, 1966).

The methoxylated dienes may be prepared from the corresponding arene derivative by metal–ammonia reduction, and react with the metal carbonyl to give XCI in yields of 70–80%. The best yields of demethoxylated aromatic derivatives are obtained when M = Cr, and the stability of the complexes follows the sequence Cr > W > Mo. The organic ligand may be liberated by the combined action of light and air.

Thus, XC may be converted into XCIII with an overall yield of 70%.

$R_1 = \alpha - H, R_2 = \alpha$ or $\beta - H$, M = Cr, W, Mo

The molybdenum complex is the most unstable, and decomplexation is observed at the ketal hydrolysis stage.

XI. ORTHO-METALLATED ARENES.
NEW SYNTHESES OF SPECIFIC ARENE
POSITIONAL ISOMERS. CARBONYLATION

A method of avoiding mixtures of positional isomers during synthesis is one of the more difficult problems in the area of arene chemistry. The selective preparation of a single isomer, for example, the ortho isomer, which is often obtained as a minor product, is not always an easy task. The use of complexes containing a heteroatom (N, P, S), where the metal atom is also bonded to the ortho position of the arene, represents an interesting contribution to the solution of specific problems of this kind.

Several reviews of ortho-metallated complexes have been published recently (Parshall, 1970; Dehand and Pfeffer, 1976; Bruce, 1977; Abicht and Issleib, 1977). This discussion is restricted to ortho-metallated complexes of demonstrated utility in organic synthesis.

The importance of metal–carbon σ bonds is no longer in doubt because of their implication in catalytic processes (Green, 1968) and because their reactivity allows the development of new routes in organic synthesis. Complexes **XCIV** to **XCVI** represent several useful structures where a metal atom replaces the hydrogen atom bonded to the ortho position of the arene. In compounds of this type, the displaced hydrogen atom may be either eliminated as H_2 or H^+, or be transferred to another atom (e.g., the metal or a different carbon) in the molecule.

(XCIV)   (XCV)   (XCVI)

Complexes **XCIV** and **XCV** both arise from the reaction of a Schiff base (Bagga et al., 1968; Murahashi et al., 1974), while **XCVI** is prepared starting from a thiobenzophenone (Alper and Des Roches, 1976). Complexes of structural type **XCVI** are the first examples of sulfur-donor ligand ortho-metallated complexes (Alper and Chan, 1973). Virtually all of the ortho-metallated complexes are air-stable and easy to handle.

The N-donor ligand complexes **(XCIV)** undergo arene carbon–metal bond cleavage by metallic hydrides. Use of deuteride reagents enables one to effect specific ortho-deuterium incorporation. Treatment of complexes such as **XCVII** with $FeCl_3$ results in carbonylation to give 1-*exo*-N-phenyl-benzisoindoline **(XCVIII)** (Flannigan *et al.*, 1969).

(XCVII)   (XCVIII)

The Schiff base complex **(XCV)** reacts with primary lithium alkyls and *tert*-butyl lithium to give ortho-alkyl substituted aromatic compounds (e.g., **XLIX**) in 30–76% yield (Murahashi *et al.*, 1974). This is particularly useful for the synthesis of *tert*-butylbenzaldehyde, which previously was prepared in low yield by a six-step process (Klouwen and Bodens, 1960).

An examination of the mechanism of this reaction led Murahashi and coworkers to the conclusion that increased product yields may be realized if the reaction is performed in the presence of a bridge dissociating ligand. A series of ortho-substituted aldehydes were obtained in 60–95% yields by treating **XCV** first with two equivalents of triphenylphosphine and then with the organolithium reagent. When secondary lithium alkyls are used, replacement of the ortho-palladium by hydrogen, and isomerization of the secondary to primary alkyl group, occur (Yamamura *et al.*, 1974).

(XCV)   (XCIX)

The ortho-alkylation reaction has been extended to azobenzenes and aromatic amines. In the several examples studied, the yields of ortho-alkylated

100 GÉRARD JAOUEN

compounds varied between 91 and 99%. A recently described route to a
variety of azobenzene-palladium derivatives increases the synthetic value of
this procedure (Cross and Tennent, 1974).

2-Phenyl-1,2,3-triazoles can be ortho-chlorinated in good yields by treatment of the heterocycle with tetrachloropalladate to give the cyclopalladated complex, followed by reaction with chlorine (Allison *et al.*, 1975).
Ortho-bromination of a cyclopalladated dithiocarbamate complex has also
been described, but the yield was not given (Cornock *et al.*, 1976).

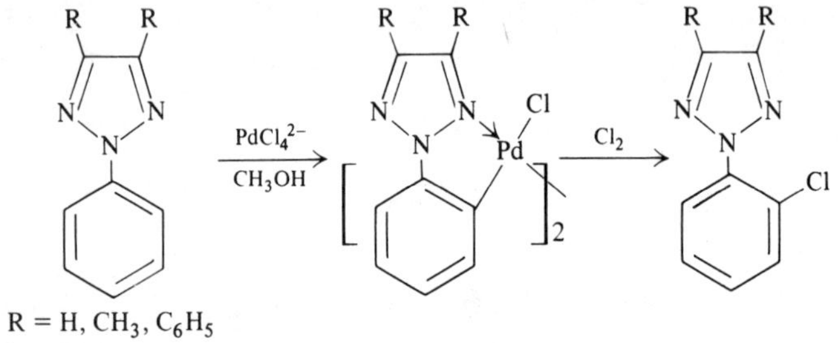

R = H, CH₃, C₆H₅

Thompson and Heck (1975) also prepared ortho palladium products of
azobenzene **(C)**, Schiff bases **(CI, CII)**, benzaldazine, acetophenone di-
methylhydrazone, 1-methyl-1-phenylhydrazones, and tertiary benzylamines.
These complexes, treated with carbon monoxide under mild conditions,
gave a variety of interesting five-membered ring heterocyclic as well as
open-chain products. Some examples are given in the following scheme:

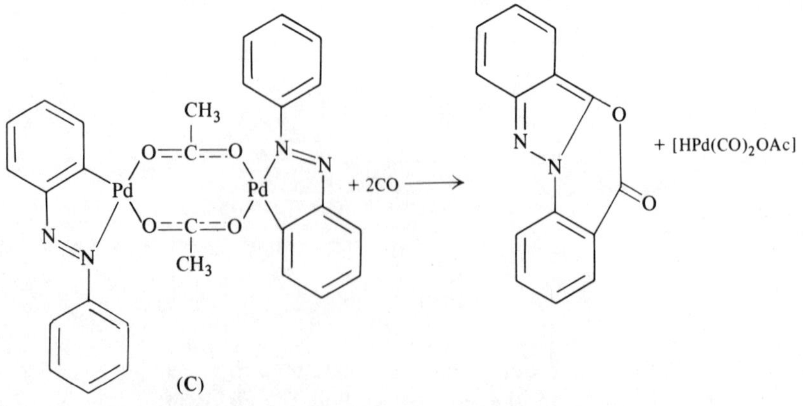

(C)

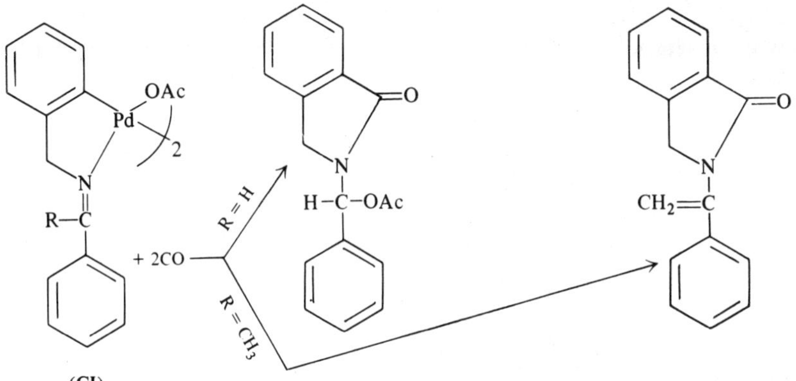

(CI)

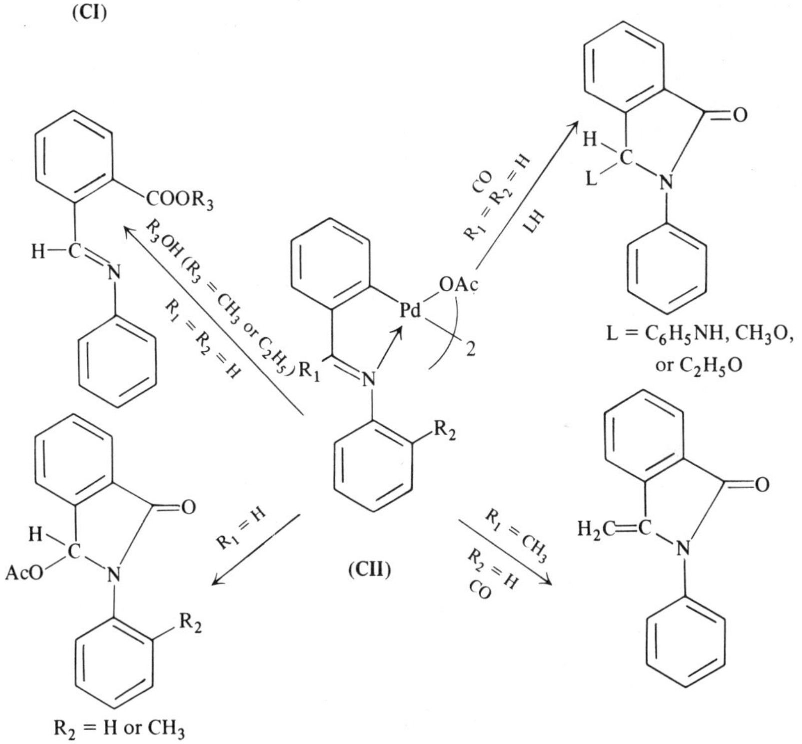

$L = C_6H_5NH, CH_3O,$
or C_2H_5O

(CII)

$R_2 = H$ or CH_3

In a series of articles (Alper, 1973, 1974, 1975; Alper and Chan, 1973; Alper and Root, 1974a,b; Alper et al., 1974), Alper has studied the reactivity of compounds such as **XCVI** and has demonstrated numerous synthetic possibilities for these complexes. These studies are particularly interesting in that starting from only one type of complex, good yields may be obtained, simply by judicious choice of reagents, of various organic compounds difficult or impossible to obtain by classical organic routes. Several of the most characteristic examples are shown in the scheme below.

A series of thiolactones (CIII) has been obtained in yields of 58–81% by treatment of complex XCVI with ceric ammonium nitrate in acetone (Alper and Chan, 1973). This complex exhibits a great propensity towards carbonyl insertion, and these thiolactones may also be prepared by other means such as treatment with $FeCl_3$, heating in ethanol, photochemical irradiation at 2537 Å, or by reaction with amines, phosphines, alcohols, or thiocyanate ion (Alper et al., 1974). Note that these thiolactones are dihydro derivatives of isobenzothiophenes, little-known heterocycles (Albert, 1959; Katritzky and Lagowsky, 1968), whose synthesis in two steps may now be facilitated.

By a simple change in the cleavage reagent, i.e., by using mercuric trifluoroacetate, H_2O_2, or m-chloroperbenzoic acid, a new synthesis of the lactones (CIV) may be realized with yields of the order of 50–75%.

If mercuric acetate is used, ortho mercuration is observed, and depending on the solvent, the initial thione is converted into an ether or ester function **(CV)** in yields of 40 to 70% (Alper and Root, 1974b). This new mode of cleavage furnishes an approach to products previously preparable only by poor routes, since it is known that the mercuric acetate group may easily be displaced by a variety of reactive species (Makarova, 1970). These points are illustrated in Scheme 10, using the syntheses of the iodide **(CVI)** (79% yield) and the cinnamic ester **(CVII)** (54% yield) (Alper and Root, 1975). The latter reaction has also been used for N-donor ligand ortho-palladated complexes (Julia *et al.*, 1975). Enones can also add to these complexes (Holton, 1977).

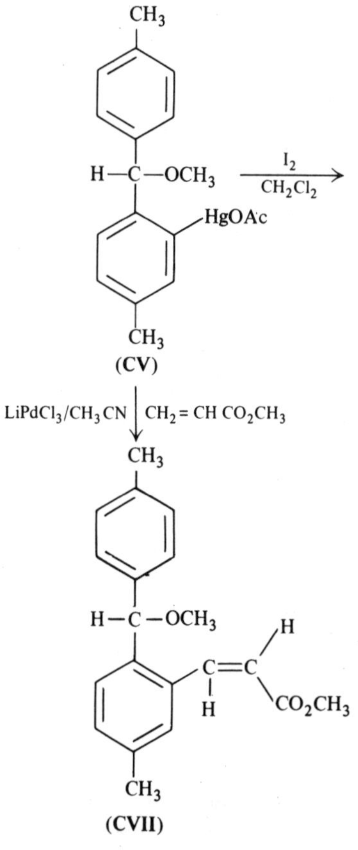

Scheme 10

The mechanism implicated in the high conversion of **XCVI** into **CIII** in the presence of either a neutral or charged nucleophile must involve, according to Alper (Alper and Root, 1975), an initial migration of the ortho-metallated σ-bonded ligand toward a terminal carbonyl group **(CVIII)**, followed by nucleophilic addition (neutral or charged) to the 16-electron complex to give **CIX** which then collapses to the thiolactone.

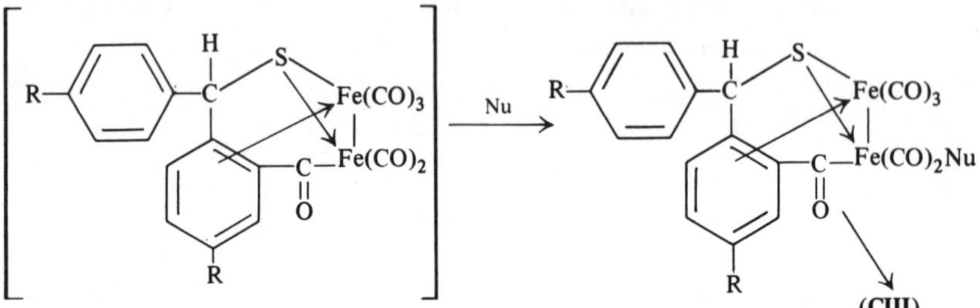

(CVIII)   (CIX)   (CIII)

Mercuric acetate plays a double role in reaction with **XCVI** (Alper and Root, 1975) (Scheme 11): cleavage of the iron–carbon σ bond (rather than ligand migration to give the product of carbonyl insertion) and mercuration of the sulfur atom to give **CX**. This complex is then converted, subject to the medium, into either an ether or an ester.

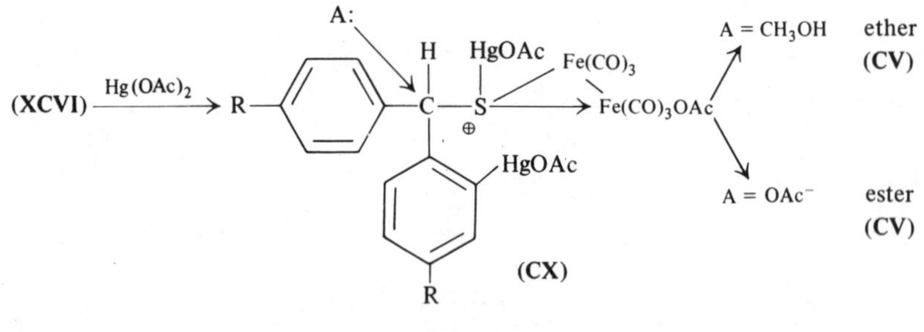

Scheme 11

Note that mercuric trifluoroacetate behaves differently (migration of the ligand as in **CVIII**, but with mercuration of the sulfur to give **CXI**). Compound **CXI** is converted into **CXII**, which gives either **CXIII** or **CIV** depending on the solvent.

Complexes of platinium and palladium related to **XCVI** have also been prepared **(CXIV)**. A new and easy preparation of mono-deuterated aromatic ketones **(CXV)** may be accomplished using complexes of the latter.

The following provides a further example of the synthetic utility of thiobenzophenones. Thus, a completely different reaction results from a change in the metal; treatment of the substituted thiobenzophenones **(CXVI)** containing attracting or moderately donating groups, with $Mn_2(CO)_{10}$ in refluxing heptane, results in desulfurization to give tetraphenylethylenes **(CXVII)** in yields of 63–69%.

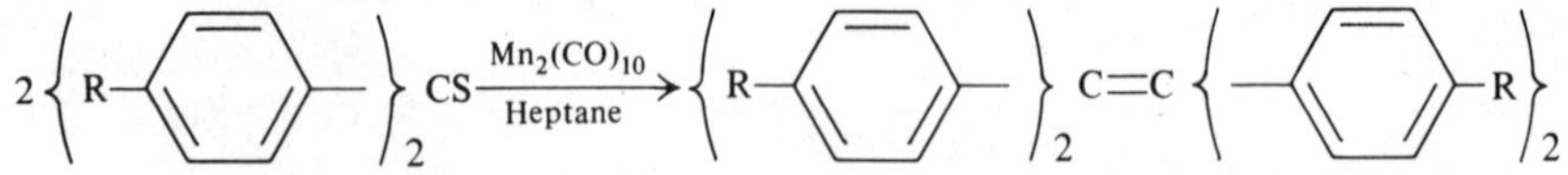

(CXVI)　　　　　　　　　　　　　　　　　　　　　　　　(CXVII)

No sulphine complexes are obtained on reaction of diarylsulphines [e.g., $(p\text{-MeOC}_6H_4)_2CSO$] with $Mn(CO)_{10}$, but deoxygenation does occur to give thiobenzophenones. Reaction with $Fe_2(CO)_9$ at room temperature also yields thiobenzophenones and/or complexes of the type **XCVI**. These reactions proceed via initial nucleophilic attack of the sulphine at a terminal metal carbonyl carbon atom (Alper, 1975).

In some of the preceding examples a molecule of CO (a one-carbon unit) has formally inserted into the M–C σ bond of the complexes. Several other examples of this type of reaction, which affords heterocycles, have been described, using, for example, palladium complexes (Takahashi and Tsuji, 1967) or octacarbonyl dicobalt as a catalyst and azobenzenes, Schiff bases, oximes, phenylhydrazones, semicarbazones, or azines as substrates (Mura-

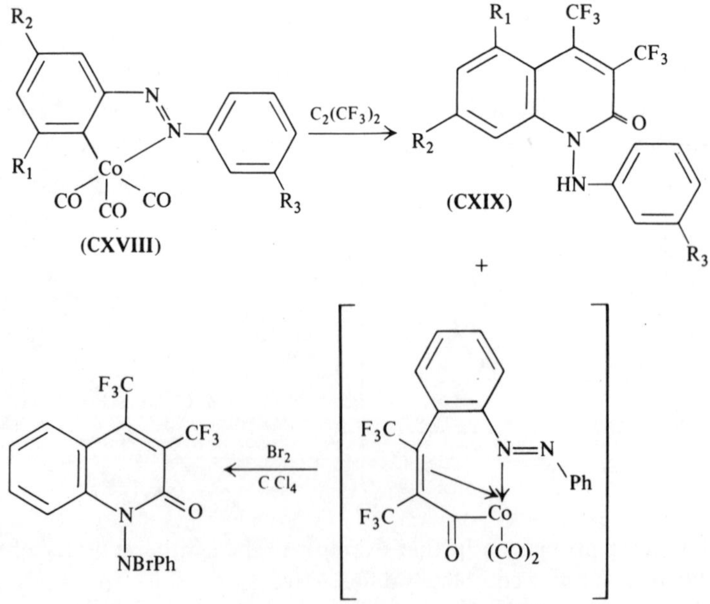

(CXVIII)　　　　　　　　　　　　　　　　　(CXIX)

+

(CXXI)　　　　　　　　　　　　　　　　　(CXX)

hashi and Horiie, 1956; Rosenthal and Wender, 1968; Heck, 1968). On the other hand, a two-carbon unit (double bond of a C_5 ring) has also been inserted between the azo function and the ortho carbon of the aryl group. Thus Russian workers (Ustynyuk and Barinov, 1970) reported that 2-chloroazobenzene reacts with $[Ni(Azb)(\eta\text{-}C_5H_5)]$ to give 4H-4-phenylcyclopenta (c) cinnoline. Recently Bruce *et al.* (1975) described the insertion of what is formally a three-carbon unit $[CO + C_2(CF_3)_2]$ into the Co–C bond of **CXVIII** and related complexes to give organic products **CXIX** formed via organometallic intermediates having the unusual structure **CXX**. The reaction between **CXVIII** and hexafluorobut-2-yne in benzene (60°, several hours) affords two products (**CXIX** and **CXX**) in proportions depending on the reaction time. After 15 to 20 hr a greatly increased yield of substituted 2-quinolones (**CXIX**) (50–70%) was obtained. Bromination of **CXX** in CCl_4 afforded the N-bromo compound (**CXXI**).

The variety of synthetic possibilities which may be envisaged should result in the rapid development of these reactions. Note that using a different principle related to the aromatic trimerization of alkynes by cobalt (Heck, 1969), benzene derivatives substituted in well defined positions (**CXXIII**) may be obtained in moderate yields (13–59%) by reaction of cobaltocyclopentadienyls (**CXXII**) (Wakatsuki *et al.*, 1974) with alkynes according to Scheme 12.

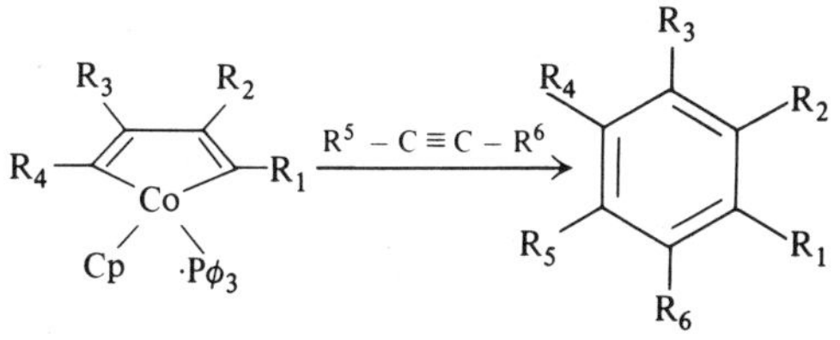

(CXXII)   (CXXIII)

Scheme 12

XII. ARENE COMPLEXES AS CATALYSTS

Arene complexes function as efficient catalysts, *inter alia*, for the polymerization (Tsutsui *et al.*, 1968), hydrogenation (Caïs *et al.*, 1968), disproportionation (Gassman and Johnson, 1977), and oxidative dimerization of unsaturated hydrocarbons (Green *et al.*, 1972). They have also proved to be useful in the study of N_2 fixation (Green and Silverthorn, 1973; Vol'pin *et al.*, 1968) and the catalytic reduction of molecular oxygen to hydrogen peroxide (Gribov *et al.*, 1971a). In these reactions, catalyst often means catalyst precursor and isolable complex which dissolves to give a catalytically active solution. Therefore, small changes in reactivity are expected to occur from different starting complexes since the same catalytic species may be generated *in situ*. For example, in metathesis of olefins by WL_6, tungsten has lost at least three ligands (L) and the complex (arene)$W(CO)_3$ gives the same stereoselectivity as $W(CO)_6$ (Basset *et al.*, 1975). However in other situations, e.g., the cleavage of ethers and reaction with acid halides, the group VI metal carbonyl $Mo(CO)_6$ is a good catalyst while the (arene)$Mo(CO)_3$ appears to be much less active (Alper and Huang, 1973).

Since catalytic applications of arene complexes have been thoroughly discussed in general reviews on organometallic catalysts (cf. Andretta *et al.*, 1970; Harmon *et al.*, 1973; Dolcetti and Hoffman, 1974; and James, 1973), this last section stresses only important or recent developments in this area.

A. Selective Hydrogenation of Dienes

The most quoted example of the catalytic behavior of π-arene $Cr(CO)_3$ derivatives is the homogeneous regioselective 1,4 hydrogenation of dienes to cis monoenes (Frankel and Butterfield, 1969; Frankel *et al.*, 1969, 1970; Caïs and Rejoan, 1970). This is of special interest in view of the high stereospecificity of the products attained in the reaction.

$$\text{Me}\diagdown\diagup\text{CO}_2\text{Me} \xrightarrow[\text{H}_2 \text{ or } \text{D}_2]{\text{Arene Cr(CO)}_3} \text{Me}\diagdown\diagup\text{CO}_2\text{Me}$$

$$\text{(CXXIV)} \qquad\qquad\qquad\qquad\qquad \text{(CXXV)}$$

The first experiments of cis hydrogenation of 1,3- and 1,4-dienes (conjugation to the 1,3-dienes precedes addition) (2×10^{-1} M) (arene catalyst: 10^{-2} M) were carried out at 100°–180° and 30–50 atm of hydrogen pressure. The order of catalytic activity of several complexes of Cr, Mo, and W has been related to the thermal stability of the complexes during hydrogenation. The activity of mesitylene $M(CO)_3$ complexes, for example, decreases in the order Mo > W > Cr and selectivity in the order Cr > Mo > W. While the catalytic activity is modified by the presence of substituents in the arene group in the order Cl > CO_2CH_3 > H > CH_3 > $(CH_3)_4$ > $(CH_3)_6$, any change of the arene moiety does not appear to greatly effect the selectivity of the system. Polystyrene anchored chromium tricarbonyl can also be used, but it offers no real advantage over homogeneous catalysts (Pittman *et al.*, 1975).

The most extensively studied model reaction was the methyl sorbate **(CXXIV)**, *trans, trans*-2,4-hexadienoate reduction into methyl 3-hexenoate **(CXXV)**. This substrate represents a suitable simple model for diene fatty acid glycerides. The mechanism has been demonstrated by deuterium tracer studies. Total arene displacement and liberation of $Cr(CO)_3$ was implied in the thermally stimulated induction step. Similar catalytically active species $[Cr(CO)_3H_2(diene)]$ can be generated photochemically from $Cr(CO)_6$ and from the thermally labile complex $Cr(CO)_3(CH_3CN)_3$ (Wrighton and Schroeder, 1973; Schroeder and Wrighton, 1974).

Linear conjugated dienes (e.g., **CXXIV**) give almost entirely cis monoenes by 1,4 addition; norbornadiene gives nortricyclene (82%) and norbornene (18%) by cis-endo addition; tricyclo[4.2.2.0]deca-3,9-diene gives both monoenes by endo addition; 12-oxa[4.4.3]propella-2,4,7,9-tetraene **(CXXVI)** gives preferentially the symmetric tetrahydrodiene **(CXXVII)** (70%), with addition from the direction of the ether oxygen (Amith *et al.*, 1973, 1975).

(CXXVI)   (CXXVII)

Recently a suitable combination of a coordinating solvent (THF, acetone, dioxane) and an arene compound with a kinetically labile π-bonded ligand (anthracene, phenanthrene, naphthalene) that undergo the expected arene displacement reaction under milder conditions has been reported by Yagupsky and Caïs (1975).

$$\text{Arene } Cr(CO)_3 + 3S \rightleftharpoons CrS_3Cr(CO)_3 + \text{Arene}$$

(CXXVIII)   **(CXXIX)**

According to these authors, the readily available and air-stable naphthalene–$Cr(CO)_3$ **(CXXVIII)** (arene = $C_{10}H_8$) complex is at present the best practical precursor for the generation of catalytically effective concentrations of the active species **CXXIX** for hydrogenation in coordinating solvents at ambient temperatures and pressures. This complex **(CXXVIII)** has also been demonstrated to be an efficient catalyst for the addition of CCl_4 to olefins (Gandolphi and Caïs, 1977).

B. 1,4-Hydrosilation of Dienes

Recently it was reported that silanes containing an Si–H bond oxidatively add to photogenerated coordinatively unsaturated metal carbonyls (Hoyano and Graham, 1972). Therefore, by analogy with the hydrogenation reaction, the possibility of achieving 1,4-hydrosilation of 1,3-dienes using $Cr(CO)_6$ as the photocatalyst was explored. Various cis allylsilanes **(CXXXII-CXXXIV)** (*vide infra*) were prepared on a synthetic scale, and in many cases, almost quantitative isolated chemical yields were obtained.

The role of the light is to generate a thermally active catalyst. This catalytic reaction can also be achieved thermally using benzene $Cr(CO)_3$ at 175°. However, though the allylsilanes obtained are common to the $Cr(CO)_6$ photochemical procedure, the products occur in different ratios and substantial yields of diene dimers are formed (Wrighton and Schroeder, 1974).

C. Olefin Polymerization

A wide range of arene complexes have been reported to induce catalytic polymerization of olefins. A benzene solution of $[(\pi\text{-}C_6H_5Me)Mo(\pi\text{-}C_3H_5)Cl]_2$ **(CXXXV)** at 60° causes quantitative polymerization of buta-1,3-diene giving the 1,2-addition polymer of repeat unit $-CH_2 \cdot CH-(CH:CH_2)-$ (Green et al., 1972).

Dibenzene chromium arene π complexes are also effective catalysts for polymerizing ethylene. These complexes are interesting examples of catalysts able to promote polymerization through different conditions. Tazima and Yuguchi (1966) used a binary catalyst system of oxygenated dibenzene chromium and organoaluminium compound. They were able to vary the molecular weights of the polymer from 50,400 to 1,660,000 by varying the temperatures (160° max) and by using $(SiO_2 - Al_2O_3)$ silica–alumina supports. The polyethylene formed was highly linear in structure, showing strong absorption at 905 cm^{-1}, which indicates a terminal vinyl polymer. This type of catalyst is not considered to be catalysis at the atomic level.

However, adding ethylene to dibenzene chromium in nitrogen-saturated heptane at 2,800 psi and 250° for 7 hr, a notable reaction was obtained (Tsutsui and Koyano, 1967). In this case, the polymer (CXXXIX) seems to contain only an internal trans double bond and the molecular weight was 34,000. Metallic chromium is formed from the thermal decomposition of dibenzenechromium. The surrounding ethylene molecules start interacting with the vacant d orbitals of the metal to form the π-bonding complex (CXXXVI) and then giving the biradical olefin chain (CXXXVII). Timms first described the direct synthesis of bis(benzene) chromium(0) in 1969 from chromium metal atoms and benzene (Timms, 1969). This new mode of access has refocused attention on the chemistry of these complexes and extensive developments may be anticipated.

Considerable work has also been devoted to catalytic properties of aromatic titanium–aluminumhalide complexes (CXL). These complexes have been reported to promote polymerization of ethylenes (Martin and Vohwinkel, 1961; Zimmer, 1966) and cyclotrimerization of butadienes (Vohwinkel, 1964) and isoprenes (Zakharkin and Akhmedov, 1969). They are able to lead to linear or cyclic polymers depending on the experimental conditions. For example, when butadiene is bubbled through a solution of $C_6H_6TiCl_2Al_2Cl_6$ in benzene, a vigorous reaction occurs. The yields of 1,5,9-cyclododecatriene (CDT), at the optimum temperature (60°–75°), are in the region of 60–65%.

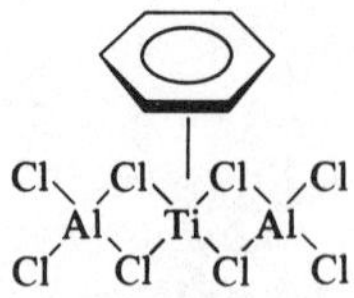

(CXL)

The proposed mechanism for the formation of CDT would involve displacement of the aromatic molecule by butadiene, followed by carbon–carbon linking and displacement of CDT.

D. Polymerization of Acetylenes

There is a striking tendency for acetylenic molecules to trimerize to aromatic products in the presence of a catalyst. This fact, at least in part, accounts for the pronounced reluctance of acetylenes to polymerize linearly to high molecular weights. However, it has been suggested that when $ArMo(CO)_3$ is used as catalyst [e.g., in Friedel-Crafts reaction (*vide infra*)], the arene ring probably stays partially on the metal in the course of the reaction. Therefore the maximum of number of acetylenes which could co-ordinate at one time is two. Farona *et al.* (1974) found that $ArM(CO)_3$ indeed promoted linear polymerization. Furthermore, the molecular weight is considerably higher than any reported to date for polyacetylenes (e.g., the rapid and quantitative polymerization of phenylacetylene (CXLI) using tol-Mo(CO)_3 (tol = toluene) as a catalyst shows a molecular weight around 12,000 versus usually 1,000 using other catalysts) (Woon and Farona, 1974).

$$C_6H_5C \equiv CH \xrightarrow[\text{cat: tol Mo(CO)}_3]{\text{neat 25 °C or benzene reflux}} [-C=CH-]_n$$
$$\underset{C_6H_5}{|}$$

(CXLI)

MW = 12,000

If $(Mes)M(CO)_3$ (mes = mesitylene; M = Cr, W) is the catalyst, the reaction proceeds much more slowly, and a ladder intermediate composed of fused cyclobutane rings (CXLII) can be isolated.

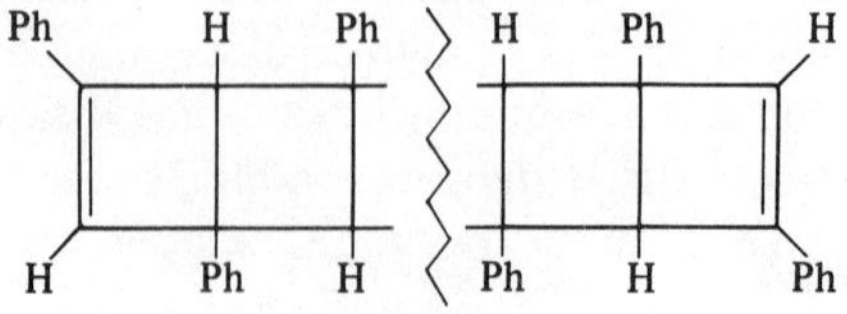

(CXLII)

The ladder compound, stable in the absence of the catalyst, breaks down in the presence of the catalyst to give the final polyconjugated compound. Available evidence indicates that the conversion of the ladder compound **(CXLII)**, likely formed from a series of $2 + 2$ cycloadditions, to polyphenyl acetylene, via a metathesis propagation, proceeds via a free-radical mechanism.

E. Friedel-Crafts Reactions

Friedel-Crafts catalysts, whether homogeneous or heterogeneous, are all Lewis acids and are capable of promoting carbonium ion formation from certain organic molecules. It might at first appear that $ArMo(CO)_3$ (Ar = arene), being a coordinatively saturated molecule, would not show Lewis acid properties. However $ArMo(CO)_3$ was shown to be an active homogeneous catalyst in such Friedel-Crafts reactions as alkylation (Scheme 13), acylation and sulfonation of aromatic systems (White and Farona, 1973) as well as dehydrohalogenation and polymerization reactions.

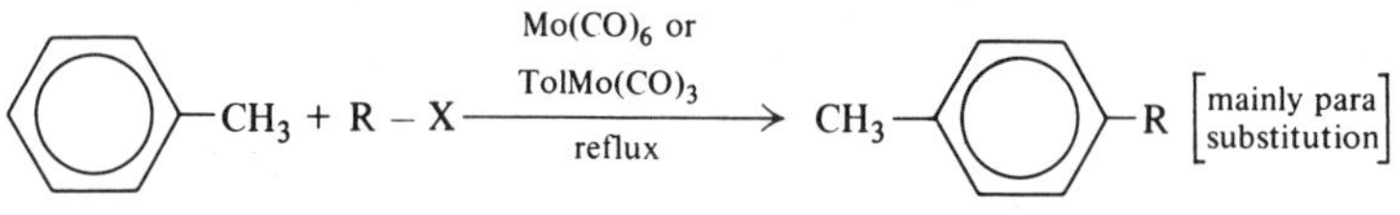

(CXLIII)   (CXLIV)

Scheme 13

The molybdenum catalysts do not necessarily promote electrophilic substitution reactions at rates faster than those of $AlCl_3$ nor are the yields any higher. These factors appear to be somewhat comparable with respect to the reactions studied so far. However, certain advantages of $ArMo(CO)_3$ over $AlCl_3$ have been observed. They are related to storage, handling, and recoverability of the catalyst at the end of the reaction. It should also be noted that in acylation reactions, $ArMo(CO)_3$ is used in catalytic amounts whereas $AlCl_3$ is not. In comparison to $MoCl_5$, toluenemolybdenum tricarbonyl is an inferior catalyst for alkylation of toluene with *tert*-butyl chloride (Tillier-Dorion and Coussemant, 1976).

Two main aspects of this kind of reaction have been discussed, namely the nature of the active catalyst and the type of the reaction. $ArMo(CO)_3$ appears to be the true catalyst, or catalyst precursor, in all reactions. However, $Mo(CO)_6$ can be used directly because it is converted *in situ* to $ArMo(CO)_3$ when heated in the presence of aromatic solvents. Although at this time a detailed mechanism cannot be proposed, White and Farona

(1973) suggested that the arene ring is still attached to the metal during the course of the reaction. A variety of experiments (e.g., the addition of radical-trapping agents or radical initiators) provides strong evidence that the type of reaction promoted by $ArMo(CO)_3$ with organic halides is ionic, rather than free radical in nature.

Polystyrenemolybdenum tricarbonyl is a less active heterogeneous catalyst, but it does exhibit better selectivity towards para substitution (Tsonis and Farona, 1976).

F. Fixation of Nitrogen

Arene complexes have also proved useful in the study of nitrogen fixation. For example, in compound **CXLV** the hydrogen ligands may be reversibly displaced by molecular nitrogen giving the dinitrogen derivatives **(CXLVI)** (Green and Silverthorn, 1973).

(CXLV)   (CXLVI)

Since there is some evidence which suggests that the enzyme nitrogenase may involve a $Mo-N_2-Fe$ system in the reduction of dinitrogen, it was of interest to prepare such a system. Treatment of the compound $[(\pi\text{-}C_5H_5)\text{-}Fe(dmpe)Me_2CO]^+BF_4^-$ in acetone with **CXLV** gives the adduct $[(\pi\text{-}C_5H_5)\text{-}Fe(dmpe)N_2(Ph_3P)_2\,Mo(MeC_6H_5)]^+BF_4^-$ with a structure essentially similar to that of the binuclear molybdenum compound **(CXLVI)**.

Vol'pin et al. (1968) found that on heating ($50°-140°$) nitrogen is capable of reacting with a mixture of $TiCl_4$, Al, and $AlBr_3$. This reaction results in catalytic reduction of the N_2 with the formation of products with metal-nitrogen bonds, hydrolysis of which yields ammonia. When the reaction is carried out in the presence of benzene as the solvent, **CXL** has been proposed as the catalyst.

G. Reduction of Molecular Oxygen

The reversible oxidation-reduction reaction $Ar_2Cr \rightleftarrows Ar_2Cr^+$ is characteristic of bis arene π-complexes of chromium. This property of chromium

π-complexes is employed in various catalyzed oxidation-reduction reactions (e.g., in the reduction of halide compounds) (Gribov *et al.*, 1971b). Bisbenzenechromium derivatives **(CXLVII)** are readily oxidized by bubbling air through a benzene solution of the complexes in the presence of water according to the equation:

$$2Ar_2Cr + O_2 + 2H_2O \longrightarrow 2Ar_2CrOH + H_2O_2$$

$$\text{(CXLVII)} \qquad\qquad\qquad \text{(CXLVIII) (CXLIX)}$$

The rate of oxidation by oxygen increases with an increase in the number of alkyl substituents attached to the aromatic ligand of the complex. The hydrogen peroxide **(CXLIX)** and alkylbenzenechromium hydroxide **(CXLVIII)** formed go into the aqueous layer (Gribov *et al.*, 1971a). The reaction can be made catalytic by addition of $Na_2S_2O_4$, which reduces the bis arene chromium cation **(CXLVIII)** back to the neutral species.

ACKNOWLEDGMENT

For helpful discussions, grateful acknowledgment is given to Dr. J. A. S. Howell.

REFERENCES

Abicht, H. P., and Issleib, K. (1977). *Z. Chem.* **17**, 1.
Albert, A. (1959). "Heterocyclic Chemistry," p. 232. Oxford Univ. Press (Athlone), London and New York.
Allison, J. A. C., El Khadem, H. S., and Wilson, C. A. (1975). *J. Heterocycl. Chem.* **12**, 1275.
Alper, H. (1973). *J. Organomet. Chem.* **61**, C62.
Alper, H. (1974). *J. Organomet. Chem.* **73**, 359.
Alper, H. (1975). *J. Organomet. Chem.* **84**, 347.
Alper, H., and Chan, A. S. K. (1973). *J. Am. Chem. Soc.* **95**, 4905.
Alper, H., and Des Roches, D. (1976). *J. Organomet. Chem.* **117**, C44.
Alper, H., and Huang, C.-C. (1973). *J. Org. Chem.* **38**, 64.
Alper, H., and Root, W. G. (1974a). *J. Chem. Soc., Chem. Commun.* p. 956.
Alper, H., and Root, W. G. (1974b). *Tetrahedron Lett.* p. 1611.
Alper, H., and Root, W. G. (1975). *J. Am. Chem. Soc.* **97**, 4251.
Alper, H., Dinkes, L. S., and Lennon, P. J., (1973). *J. Organomet. Chem.* **57**, C12.
Alper, H., Root, W. G., and Chan, A. S. K. (1974). *J. Organomet. Chem.* **71**, C14.
Amith, C., Caïs, M., Frankel, D., and Ginsburg, D. (1973). *Heterocycles* **1**, 39.
Amith, C., Caïs, M., Frankel, D., and Ginsburg, D. (1975). *Heterocycles* **3**, 25.
Andretta, A., Conti, F., and Ferrari, G. F. (1970). *In* "Aspects of Homogeneous Catalysis" (R. Ugo, ed.) Vol. 1, p. 204 et seq. Carlo Manfredi, Milan.
Ashraf, M. (1972). *Can. J. Chem.* **50**, 118.
Ashraf, M., and Jackson, W. R. (1972). *J. Chem. Soc. Perkin Trans. 2* p. 103.

Bagga, M. M., Flannigan, W. T., Knox, G. R., Pauson, P. L., Preston, F. J., and Reed, R. I. (1968). *J. Chem. Soc. C* p. 36.

Basset, J. M., Bilhou, J. L., Mutin, R., and Theolier, A. (1975). *J. Am. Chem. Soc.* **97**, 7376.

Bear, C. A., Cullen, W. R., Kutney, J. P., Ridaura, V. E., Trotter, J., and Zanarotti, A. (1973). *J. Am. Chem. Soc.* **95**, 3058.

Besançon, J., Top, S., Tirouflet, J., Gautheron, B., and Dusausoy, Y. (1975). *J. Organomet. Chem.* **94**, 35.

Birch, A. J., and Jenkins, I. D. (1975). *Tetrahedron Lett.* p. 119.

Birch, A. J., Cross, P. E., and Fitton, H. (1965). *Chem. Commun.* p. 366.

Birch, A. J., Cross, P. E., Connor, D. T., and Subba Rao, G. S. R. (1966). *J. Chem. Soc. C* p. 54.

Birch, A. J., Jenkins, I. D., and Liepa, A. J. (1975). *Tetrahedron Lett.* p. 1723.

Block, T. F., Fenske, R. F., and Casey, C. P. (1976). *J. Am. Chem. Soc.* **98**, 441.

Bly, R. S., and Veazey, R. L. (1969). *J. Am. Chem. Soc.* **91**, 4221.

Bly, R. S., Strickland, R. C., Swindell, R. T., and Veazey, R. L. (1970). *J. Am. Chem. Soc.* **92**, 3722.

Bodner, G. M., and Todd, L. J. (1974). *Inorg. Chem.* **13**, 360.

Boyle, P. H. (1971). *Q. Rev., Chem. Soc.* **25**, 323.

Braun, S., and Watts, W. E. (1975). *J. Organomet. Chem.* **84**, C33.

Brown, B. R., and White, A. M. S. (1957). *J. Chem. Soc.* p. 3755.

Brown, D. A., and Carroll, D. G. (1965). *J. Chem. Soc.* p. 2822.

Brown, D. A., and Raju, J. R. (1966). *J. Chem. Soc. A* p. 40.

Brown, D. A., and Rawlinson, R. M. (1969). *J. Chem. Soc. A* p. 1530.

Brown, D. A., and Sloan, H. (1962). *J. Chem. Soc.* p. 3849.

Bruce, M. I. (1977). *Angew. Chem., Int. Ed. Engl.* **16**, 73.

Bruce, M. I., Goodall, B. L., and Stone, F. G. A. (1975). *J. Chem. Soc., Dalton Trans.* p. 1651.

Bunnett, J. F. (1958). *Q. Rev., Chem. Soc.* **12**, 1.

Bunnett, J. F. (1962). *Angew. Chem., Int. Ed. Engl.* **1**, 225.

Bunnett, J. F., and Hermann, H. (1971). *J. Org. Chem.* **36**, 4081.

Burgstahler, A., Malfer, D. J., and Abdelrahman, M. O. (1965). *Tetrahedron Lett.* p. 1625.

Caillet, P., and Jaouen, G. (1975). *J. Organomet. Chem.* **91**, C53.

Caïs, M., and Rejoan, A. (1970). *Inorg. Chim. Acta* **4**, 509.

Caïs, M., Frankel, E. N., and Rejoan, A. (1968). *Tetrahedron Lett.* p. 1919.

Card, R. J., and Trahanovsky, W. S. (1973). *Tetrahedron Lett.* p. 3823.

Caro, B., and Jaouen, G. (1974). *Tetrahedron Lett.* p. 1229.

Carroll, D. G., and McGlynn, S. P. (1968). *Inorg. Chem.* **7**, 1285.

Casey, C. P., and Bunnell, C. A. (1976). *J. Am. Chem. Soc.* **98**, 436.

Castro, C. E., Andrews, L. J., and Keefer, R. M. (1958). *J. Am. Chem. Soc.* **80**, 2322.

Ceccon, A. (1971). *J. Organomet. Chem.* **29**, C19.

Ceccon, A. (1974). *J. Organomet. Chem.* **72**, 189.

Ceccon, A., and Biserni, G. S. (1972). *J. Organomet. Chem.* **39**, 313.

Ceccon, A., and Catelani, G. (1974). *J. Organomet. Chem.* **72**, 179.

Ceccon, A., and Sartori, S. (1973). *J. Organomet. Chem.* **50**, 161.

Connelly, N. G., and Kelly, R. L. (1974). *J. Chem. Soc., Dalton Trans.* p. 2334.

Cornelisse, J., and Havinga, E. (1975). *Chem. Rev.* **75**, 353.

Cornock, M. C., Davis, R. C., Leaver, D., and Stephenson, T. A. (1976). *J. Organomet. Chem.* **107**, C43.

Cross, R. J., and Tennent, N. H. (1974). *J. Organomet. Chem.* **72**, 21.

Dabard, R., and Jaouen, G. (1969). *Tetrahedron Lett.* p. 3391.

Dabard, R., and Jaouen, G. (1974). *Bull. Soc. Chim. Fr.* p. 1639.

Dabard, R., and Meyer, A. (1967). *C.R. Hebd. Seances Acad. Sci., Ser. C* **264**, 903.

Dabard, R., Meyer, A., and Jaouen, G. (1969). *C.R. Hebd. Seances Acad. Sci., Ser. C* **268**, 201.
Davis, R. E., Simpson, H. D., Grice, N., and Pettit, R. (1971). *J. Am. Chem. Soc.* **93**, 6688.
Dehand, J., and Pfeffer, M. (1976). *Coord. Chem. Rev.* **18**, 327.
des Abbayes, H., and Boudeville, M. A., (1977). *J. Org. Chem.* **42**, 4104.
Dolcetti, G., and Hoffman, N. W. (1974). *Inorg. Chim. Acta* **9**, 269.
Efraty, A., and Maitlis, P. M. (1967). *J. Am. Chem. Soc.* **89**, 3744.
Emanuel, R. V., and Randall, E. W. (1969). *J. Chem. Soc. A* p. 3002.
Ercoli, R., Calderazzo, F., and Mantica, E. (1959). *Chim. Ind. (Milan)* **41**, 404.
Falk, H., Schlögl, K., and Steyrer, W. (1966). *Monatsh. Chem.* **97**, 1029.
Farona, M. F., Lofgren, P. A., and Woon, P. S. (1974). *J. Chem. Soc., Chem. Commun.* p. 246.
Fischer, E. O., and Ofele, K. (1967). *J. Organomet. Chem.* **8**, P5.
Fischer, E. O., and Schmidt, M. W. (1967). *Chem. Ber.* **100**, 3782.
Fischer, E. O., and Schreiner, S. (1959). *Chem. Ber.* **92**, 939.
Fischer, E. O., Essler, H., Frohlich, W., Mortensen, J. P., and Semmlinger, W. (1958). *Chem. Ber.* **91**, 2763.
Flannigan, W. T., Knox, G. R., and Pauson, P. L. (1969). *J. Chem. Soc. C* p. 2077.
Fletcher, J. L., and McGlinchey, M. J. (1975). *Can. J. Chem.* **53**, 1525.
Frankel, E. N., and Butterfield, R. O. (1969). *J. Org. Chem.* **34**, 3930.
Frankel, E. N., Selke, E., and Glass, C. A. (1969). *J. Org. Chem.* **34**, 3936.
Frankel, E. N., Thomas, F. L., and Cowan, J. C. (1970). *J. Am. Oil Chem. Soc.* **47**, 497.
Fritz, H. P., and Kreiter, C. G. (1967). *J. Organomet. Chem.* **7**, 427.
Gandolfi, O., and Caïs, M. (1977). *J. Organomet. Chem.* **125**, 191.
Gassman, P. G., and Johnson, T. H. (1977). *J. Am. Chem. Soc.* **99**, 622.
Goasmat, F., Dabard, R., and Patin, H. (1975). *Tetrahedron Lett.* p. 2359.
Green, M. L. H. (1968). "Organometallic Compounds," Vol. 2, Chapters 7 and 9. Methuen, London.
Green, M. L. H., and Silverthorn, W. E. (1973). *J. Chem. Soc., Dalton Trans.* p. 301.
Green, M. L. H., Knight, J., Mitchard, L. C., Roberts, G. C., and Silverthorn, W. E. (1972). *J. Chem. Soc., Chem. Commun.* p. 987.
Gribov, B. G., Mozzhukhin, D. D., Suskina, I. A., and Salamatin, B. A. (1971a). *Dokl. Akad. Nauk SSSR* **196**, 586.
Gribov, B. G., Mozzhukhin, D. D., Kozyrkhin, B. I., and Gubin, S. P. (1971b). *Proc. Int. Conf. Organomet. Chem., 5th, 1971* **I**, 82.
Gubin, S. P., and Khandkarova, V. S. (1970). *J. Organomet. Chem.* **22**, 449.
Gubin, S. P., Khandkarova, V. S., and Kreindlin, A. Z. (1974). *J. Organomet. Chem.* **64**, 229.
Hackett, P., and Jaouen, G. (1975). *Inorg. Chim. Acta* **12**, L19.
Harmon, R. E., Gupta, S. K., and Brown, D. J. (1973). *Chem. Rev.* **73**, 21.
Heck, R. F. (1968). *J. Am. Chem. Soc.* **90**, 313.
Heck, R. F. (1969). *Acc. Chem. Res.* **2**, 10, and references therein.
Helling, J. F., and Braitsch, D. M. (1970). *J. Am. Chem. Soc.* **92**, 7207.
Helling, J. F., and Cash, G. S. (1974). *J. Organomet. Chem.* **73**, C10.
Herberich, G. E., and Fischer, E. O. (1962). *Chem. Ber.* **95**, 2803.
Holmes, J. D., Jones, D. A. K., and Pettit, R. (1965). *J. Organomet. Chem.* **4**, 324.
Holton, R. A. (1977). *Tetrahedron Lett.* p. 355.
Howell, J. A. S., Johnson, B. F. G., and Lewis, J. (1974). *J. Chem. Soc., Dalton Trans.* p. 293.
Hoyano, J. K., and Graham, W. A. G. (1972). *Inorg. Chem.* **11**, 1265, and references cited therein.
Ingersoll, A. W. (1944). *Org. React.* **2**, 376.
Jackson, W. R., and Jennings, W. B. (1969). *J. Chem. Soc. B* p. 1221.
Jackson, W. R., and Mitchell, T. R. B. (1969). *J. Chem. Soc. B* p. 1228.

James, B. R. (1973). "Homogeneous Hydrogenation." Wiley, New York.
Jaouen, G. (1973). Thése d'Etat.
Jaouen, G., and Dabard, R. (1970). *J. Organomet. Chem.* **21**, P43.
Jaouen, G., and Dabard, R. (1971). *Tetrahedron Lett.* p. 1015.
Jaouen, G., and Dabard, R. (1974a). *J. Organomet. Chem.* **72**, 377.
Jaouen, G., and Dabard, R. (1974b). *Bull. Soc. Chim. Fr.* p. 1646.
Jaouen, G., and Meyer, A. (1975). *J. Am. Chem. Soc.* **97**, 4667.
Jaouen, G., and Meyer, A. (1976). *Tetrahedron Lett.* p. 3547.
Jaouen, G., and Simonneaux, G. (1973). *J. Organomet. Chem.* **61**, C39.
Jaouen, G., Tchissambou, L., and Dabard, R. (1972). *C.R. Hebd. Seances Acad. Sci., Ser. C* **274**, 654.
Jaouen, G., Caro, B., and Le Bihan, J. Y. (1972). *C.R. Hebd. Seances Acad. Sci., Ser. C* **274**, 904.
Jaouen, G., Meyer, A., and Simonneaux, G. (1975). *J. Chem. Soc., Chem. Commun.* p. 814.
John, G. R., Kane-Maguire, L. A. P., and Eaborn, C. (1975). *J. Chem. Soc., Chem. Commun.* p. 481.
Jonczyk, A., Ludwikow, M., and Makosza, M. (1973). *Rocz. Chem.* **47**, 89.
Jones, D., and Wilkinson, G. (1964). *J. Chem. Soc.* p. 2479, and references cited therein.
Julia, M., Le Goffic, F., Igolen, J., and Braillage, M. (1969). *Tetrahedron Lett.* p. 1569.
Julia, M., Duteil, M., and Lallemand, J. Y. (1975). *J. Organomet. Chem.* **102**, 239.
Kane-Maguire, L. A. P., and Mansfield, C. A. (1973). *J. Chem. Soc., Chem. Commun.* p. 540.
Kang, J. W., and Maitlis, P. M. (1971). *J. Organomet. Chem.* **30**, 127.
Katritzky, A. R., and Lagowski, J. M. (1968). "Principles of Heterocyclic Chemistry." Academic Press, New York.
Khand, I. U., Pauson, P. L., and Watts, W. E. (1969). *J. Chem. Soc. C* p. 2024.
Khandkarova, V. S., and Gubin, S. P. (1970). *J. Organomet. Chem.* **22**, 149.
Khandkarova, V. S., Gubin, S. P., and Kvasov, B. A. (1970). *J. Organomet. Chem.* **23**, 509.
Klouwen, M. H., and Bodens, H. (1960). *Recl. Trav. Chim. Pays-Bas* **79**, 1029.
Koridze, A. A., Petrovskii, P. V., Gubin, S. P., and Fedin, E. I. (1975). *J. Organomet. Chem.* **93**, C26.
Kreindlin, A. Z., Khandkarova, V. S., and Gubin, S. P. (1975). *J. Organomet. Chem.* **92**, 197.
Kursanov, D. N., Setkina, V. N., Baranetskaya, N. K., Zdanovitch, V. I., and Anisimov, K. N. (1970). *Dokl. Akad. Nauk SSSR* **190**, 1103.
Kursanov, D. N., Setkina, V. N., and Gribov, B. G. (1972). *J. Organomet. Chem.* **37**, C35.
Kutney, J. P. (1977). *Heterocycles* **7**, 593.
Kutney, J. P., Greenhouse, R., and Ridaura, V. E. (1974). *J. Am. Chem. Soc.* **96**, 7364.
McFarlane, W., and Grim, S. O. (1966). *J. Organomet. Chem.* **5**, 147.
Mandelbaum, A., Neuwirth, Z., and Caïs, M. (1963). *Inorg. Chem.* **2**, 902.
Mansfield, C. A., Al-Kathumi, K. M., and Kane-Maguire, L. A. P. (1974). *J. Organomet. Chem.* **71**, C11.
Makarova, L. G. (1970). *Organomet. React.* **1**, 119.
Martin, H., and Vohwinkel, F. (1961). *Chem. Ber.* **94**, 2416.
Meyer, A. (1973). *Ann. Chim. (Paris [1Y])* **8**, 397.
Meyer, A., and Dabard, R. (1972). *J. Organomet. Chem.* **36**, C38.
Meyer, A., and Jaouen, G. (1974). *J. Chem. Soc., Chem. Commun.* p. 787.
Meyer, A., and Jaouen, G. (1975). *J. Organomet. Chem.* **97**, C21.
Meyer, A., Jaouen, G., and Dabard, R. (1971). *Proc. Int. Congr. Organomet. Chem., 5th, 1971* **II**, 222.
Meyer, A., Neudeck, H., and Schlögl, K. (1977). *Chem. Ber.* **110**, 1403.
Miller, R. G., Fahey, D. R., and Kuhlman, D. P. (1968). *J. Am. Chem. Soc.* **90**, 6248.

Mori, M., and Ban, Y. (1976a). *Tetrahedron Lett.* p. 1803.
Mori, M., and Ban, Y. (1976b). *Tetrahedron Lett.* p. 1807.
Munro, J. D., and Pauson, P. L. (1961). *J. Chem. Soc.* p. 3475.
Murahashi, S., and Horiie, S. (1956). *J. Am. Chem. Soc.* **78**, 4816.
Murahashi, S. I., Tanba, Y., Yamamura, M., and Moritani, I. (1974). *Tetrahedron Lett.* p. 3749.
Nesmeyanov, A. N., Vol'kenau, N. A., and Bolejova, I. N. (1967). *Dokl. Akad. Nauk SSSR* **175**, 606.
Neuse, W. E. (1975). *J. Organomet. Chem.* **99**, 287.
Nicholls, B., and Whiting, M. C. (1959). *J. Chem. Soc.* p. 551.
Nystrom, R. F. (1955). *J. Am. Chem. Soc.* **77**, 2544.
Nystrom, R. F., and Berger, C. R. A. (1958). *J. Am. Chem. Soc.* **80**, 2896.
Ofele, K. (1967). *Angew. Chem., Int. Ed. Engl.* **6**, 988.
Parshall, G. W. (1970). *Acc. Chem. Res.* **3**, 139.
Pauson, P. L., and Segal, J. A. (1975). *J. Chem. Soc., Dalton Trans.* p. 1677.
Pittman, C. U., Jr., Kim, B. T., and Douglas, W. M. (1975). *J. Org. Chem.* **40**, 590.
Price, J. T., and Sorensen, T. S. (1968). *Can. J. Chem.* **46**, 515.
Rausch, M. D. (1974). *J. Org. Chem.* **39**, 1787.
Rosenthal, A., and Wender, I. (1968). *In* "Organic Syntheses via Metal Carbonyls" (I. Wender and P. Pino, eds.), Vol. 1, p. 405. Wiley (Interscience), New York.
Ross, A. (1963). *Prog. Phys. Org. Chem.* **1**, 31.
Rossi, R. A., and Bunnett, J. F. (1973). *J. Org. Chem.* **38**, 1407.
Rubezhov, A. Z., and Gubin, S. P. (1972). *Adv. Organomet. Chem.* **10**, 347 et seq.
Saillard, J. Y., Choplin, F., Kaufmann, G., and Grandjean, D. (1974). *J. Mol. Struct.* **23**, 363.
Sauer, R., and Visgen, H. (1960). *Angew. Chem.* **72**, 294.
Schlögl, K., Mohar, A., and Peterlik, M. (1961). *Monatsh. Chem.* **92**, 921.
Schroeder, M. A., and Wrighton, M. S. (1974). *J. Organomet. Chem.* **74**, 29.
Semmelhack, M. F., and Clark, G. (1977). *J. Am. Chem. Soc.* **99**, 1675.
Semmelhack, M. F., and Hall, H. T. (1974a). *J. Am. Chem. Soc.* **96**, 7092.
Semmelhack, M. F., and Hall, H. T. (1974b). *J. Am. Chem. Soc.* **96**, 7097.
Semmelhack, M. F., Helquist, P. M., and Jones, L. D. (1971). *J. Am. Chem. Soc.* **93**, 5908.
Semmelhack, M. F., Chong, B. P., and Jones, L. D. (1972). *J. Am. Chem. Soc.* **94**, 8629.
Semmelhack, M. F., Helquist, P. M., and Gorzynski, J. D. (1972b). *J. Am. Chem. Soc.* **94**, 9234.
Semmelhack, M. F., Stauffer, R. D., and Rogerson, T. D. (1973). *Tetrahedron Lett.* p. 4519.
Semmelhack, M. F., Hall, H. T., Yoshifuji, M., and Clark, G. (1975). *J. Am. Chem. Soc.* **97**, 1247.
Semmelhack, M. F., Hall, H. T., Jr., and Yoshifuji, M. (1976). *J. Am. Chem. Soc.* **98**, 6387.
Seyferth, D., and Eschbach, C. S. (1975). *J. Organomet. Chem.* **94**, C5.
Shvo, Y., and Hazum, E. (1974). *J. Chem. Soc., Chem. Commun.* p. 336.
Silverthorn, W. E. (1975). *Adv. Organomet. Chem.* **13**, 47.
Slocum, D. W., and Engelmann, T. R. (1972). *J. Am. Chem. Soc.* **94**, 8596.
Sutherland, R. G. (1977). *J. Organomet. Chem. Libr.* **3**, 311.
Sutherland, R. G., Chen, S. C., Pannekoek, W. J., and Lee, C. C. (1975). *J. Organomet. Chem.* **101**, 221.
Sutherland, R. G., Pannekoek, W. J., and Lee, C. C. (1977). *J. Organomet. Chem.* **129**, C1.
Sweigart, D. A., Gower, M., and Kane-Maguire, L. A. P. (1976). *J. Organomet. Chem.* **108**, C15.
Takahashi, H., and Tsuji, J. (1967). *J. Organomet. Chem.* **10**, 511.
Tazima, Y., and Yuguchi, S. (1966). *Bull. Chem. Soc. Jpn.* **39**, 2534.
Tchissambou, L., Jaouen, G., and Dabard, R. (1972). *C.R. Hebd. Seances Acad. Sci., Ser. C* **274**, 806.
Thompson, J. M., and Heck, R. F. (1975). *J. Org. Chem.* **40**, 2667.

Tillier-Dorion, F., and Coussemant, F. (1976). *Bull. Soc. Chim. Fr.* p. 1116.
Timms, P. L. (1969). *Chem. Commun.* p. 1033.
Trahanovsky, W. S., and Card, R. J. (1972). *J. Am. Chem. Soc.* **94**, 2897.
Trahanovsky, W. S., and Wells, D. K. (1969). *J. Am. Chem. Soc.* **91**, 5870.
Tsonis, C. P., and Farona, M. F. (1976). *J. Organomet. Chem.* **114**, 293.
Tsutsui, M., and Koyano, T. (1967). *J. Polym. Sci., Part A-1* **5**, 683.
Tsutsui, M., Aryoshi, J., Koyano, T., and Levy, M. N. (1968). *Adv. Chem. Ser.* **70**, 266.
Ugo, R. (1973). *Proc. Int. Congr. Catal., 5th, 1972.*
Ustynyuk, Y. A., and Barinov, I. V. (1970). *J. Organomet. Chem.* **23**, 551.
Vohwinkel, F. (1964). *Trans. N.Y. Acad. Sci.* [2] **26**, 446.
Vol'pin, M. E., Ilatovskaya, M. A., Kosyakova, L. V., and Shur, V. B. (1968). *Dokl. Akad. Nauk SSSR* **180**, 103.
Wakatsuki, Y., Kuramitsu, T., and Yamazaki, Y. (1974). *Tetrahedron Lett.* p. 4549.
Walker, P. J. C., and Mawby, R. J. (1971). *Inorg. Chem.* **10**, 404.
Walker, P. J. C., and Mawby, R. J. (1973a). *J. Chem. Soc., Dalton Trans.* p. 622.
Walker, P. J. C., and Mawby, R. J. (1973b). *Inorg. Chim. Acta* **7**, 621.
White, J. F., and Farona, M. F. (1973). *J. Organomet. Chem.* **63**, 329.
Wilen, S. H. (1971). *Top. Stereochem.* **6**, 107.
Woon, P. S., and Farona, M. F. (1974). *J. Polym. Sci.* **12**, 1749.
Wrighton, M. S., and Schroeder, M. A. (1973). *J. Am. Chem. Soc.* **95**, 5764.
Wrighton, M. S., and Schroeder, M. A. (1974). *J. Am. Chem. Soc.* **96**, 6235.
Wu, A., Biehl, E. R., and Reeves, P. C. (1971). *J. Organomet. Chem.* **33**, 53.
Wu, A., Biehl, E. R., and Reeves, P. C. (1972). *J. Chem. Soc., Perkin Trans.* 2p. 449.
Wurbels, G. G., and Letsinger, R. L. (1974). *J. Am. Chem. Soc.* **96**, 6698.
Yagupsky, G., and Caïs, M. (1975). *Inorg. Chim. Acta* **12**, L27.
Yamamura, M., Moritani, I., and Murahashi, S. I. (1974). *Chem. Lett.* p. 1423.
Zakharkin, L. I., and Akhmedov, V. M. (1969). *Az. Khim. Zh.* **2**, 58.
Zeiss, H., Wheatley, P. J., and Winkler, H. J. S. (1966). "Benzenoïd-Metal Complexes," Chapter 3. Ronald, New York.
Zimmer, H. J. (1966). Verfahrenstechnik Fr. 1,460,233; *Chem. Abstr.* **67**, P11928.

3

OXIDATION, REDUCTION, REARRANGEMENT, AND OTHER SYNTHETICALLY USEFUL PROCESSES

HOWARD ALPER

Copyright © 1978 by Academic Press, Inc.
All rights of reproduction in any form reserved.
ISBN 0–12–053102–X

This chapter is concerned with useful reactions which have not been discussed, or only briefly mentioned, in other chapters.

I. OXIDATION

Oxidative cleavage of olefinic, carbene, and arene metal complexes is discussed in the appropriate chapters. Excellent, general reviews of metal-catalyzed oxidations have recently been published (Sheldon and Kochi, 1976; Tolstikov *et al.*, 1975).

A. Olefins and Alkynes

Molybdenum hexacarbonyl is a useful catalyst for the epoxidation of olefins by *tert*-butyl, *tert*-amyl, or cumene hydroperoxide (Sheng and Zajacek, 1968a, 1970; Sheng, 1972; Descotes and Legrand, 1972; Tolstikov *et al.*, 1973; Spadlo, 1974). Other useful catalysts include molybdenum pentachloride and vanadium oxyacetylacetonate. Benzene is generally used as the reaction solvent although the rate of epoxidation of allyl chloride [$(CH_3)_3COOH$, $Mo(CO)_6$] has been found to be greatest in chlorinated solvents (1,1,2,2-tetrachloroethane > benzene > N,N-dimethylformamide) (Sheldon *et al.*, 1973). The rate of epoxidation generally increases with increasing substitution at the double bond, enabling preferential reaction to occur in some cases. For example, only the trisubstituted double bond of limonene underwent epoxidation by *tert*-amyl hydroperoxide to give the monoepoxides **II** and **III** in a ratio of 3:7 (71% yield) (Yur'ev *et al.*, 1975).

With perbenzoic acid, **II** and **III** were formed in a 1:1 ratio. Much higher stereoselectivity has been observed in the Mo(CO)$_6$-catalyzed epoxidation of *p*-menth-1-ene **(IV)** and several other monoterpenes (Yur'ev *et al.*, 1974): 3-cyclohexen-1-ol **(V**, Sharpless and Michaelson, 1973), *trans*-3-

penten-2-ol **(VI**, Tanaka *et al.*, 1974), and in the remote epoxidation of certain steroid olefins **(VII**, Breslow and Maresca, 1977).

Hydroxy ketones (e.g., **IX**) can be prepared in good yields by Mo(CO)$_6$-catalyzed reaction of olefins such as α-cedrene **(VIII)** with excess *tert*-amyl hydroperoxide. These reactions proceed via an epoxide intermediate (Tolstikov *et al.*, 1971b).

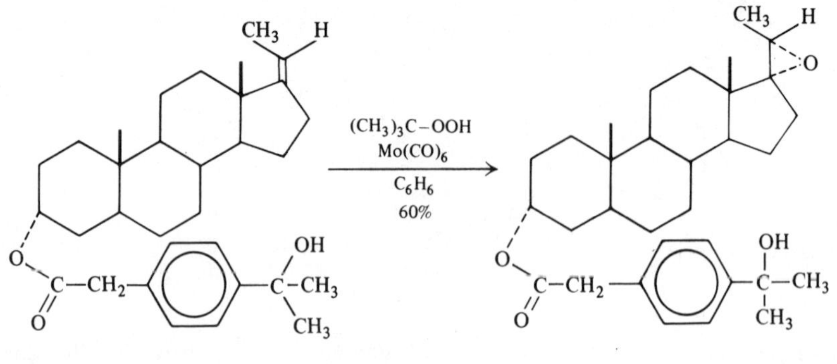

(VII)

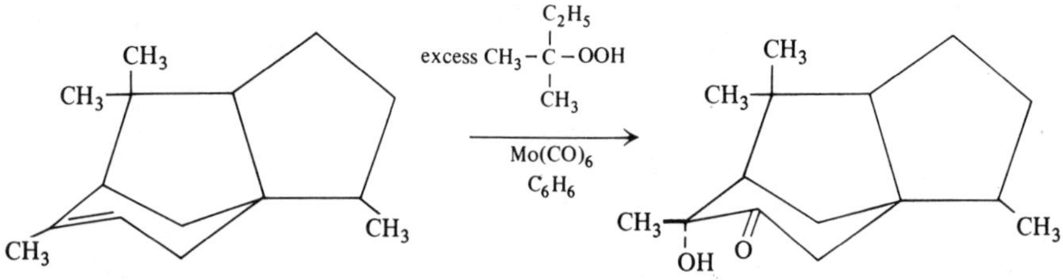

(VIII)   (IX)

It is claimed that the rate of epoxidation can be increased by preheating the olefin-catalyst mixture to reflux and then adding the hydroperoxide (Harrod *et al.*, 1972). The active Mo(VI) catalyst was isolated using propene as the olefin (Sheldon, 1973b). Similarly, a W(VI) species is the active catalyst derived from W(CO)$_6$ (Sheldon and Van Doorn, 1973). On the basis of kinetic studies (Sheldon, 1973a; Baker *et al.*, 1973), it has been proposed that Mo(VI), once generated from Mo(CO)$_6$, reacts with the hydroperoxide to give X. Reaction of the latter with the olefin affords the epoxide.

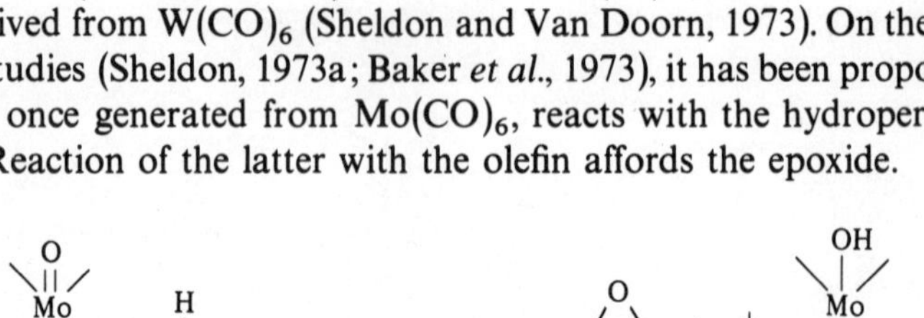

(X)

Evidence against the intermediacy of X comes from a study of the molybdenum- and vanadium-catalyzed epoxidation of olefins [e.g., (E)-

cyclododecene **XI**] by *tert*-butyl hydroperoxide in the presence of ^{18}O-enriched water (Chong and Sharpless, 1977). No incorporation of

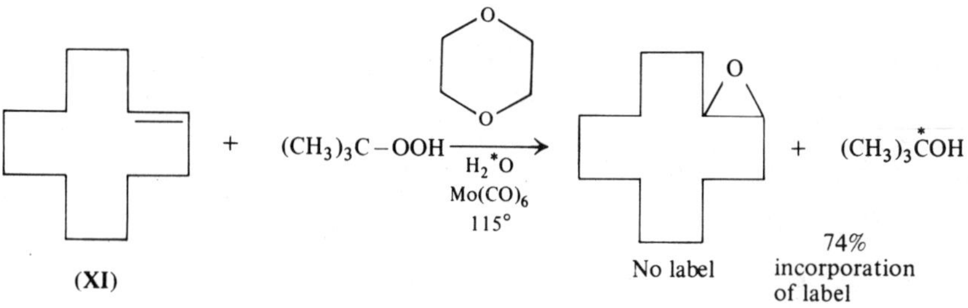

$$\text{(XI)} \quad + \quad (CH_3)_3C-OOH \xrightarrow[\substack{H_2{}^*O \\ Mo(CO)_6 \\ 115°}]{} \quad + \quad (CH_3)_3\overset{*}{C}OH$$

(XI)   No label   74% incorporation of label

labeled oxygen was observed in the resultant epoxide, indicating that the intact alkyl hydroperoxide is present in the activated complex. Therefore, mechanism **XII**, or a related mechanism, may be valid.

Styrene oxide was obtained in low yield by the oxygenation of styrene catalyzed by Vaska's complex [Ir(CO)Cl(PPh$_3$)$_2$], the major products being

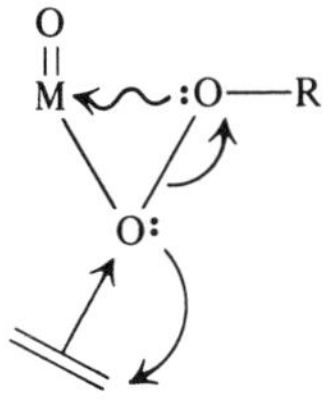

(XII)

benzaldehyde and formaldehyde (Lyons and Turner, 1972a). Increased amounts of styrene oxide resulted when Rh(CO)Cl(PPh$_3$)$_2$ was used as the catalyst. The latter catalyst induced a similar reaction with tetramethylethylene, giving the epoxide in 25% yield (Lyons and Turner, 1972b). Cyclopentadienyl vanadium tetracarbonyl catalyzes the stereoselective oxidation of cyclohexene to *cis*-1,2-epoxycyclohexan-3-ol **(XIII)**, but it remains to be seen whether this reaction is a general one (Lyons, 1974). The oxygena-

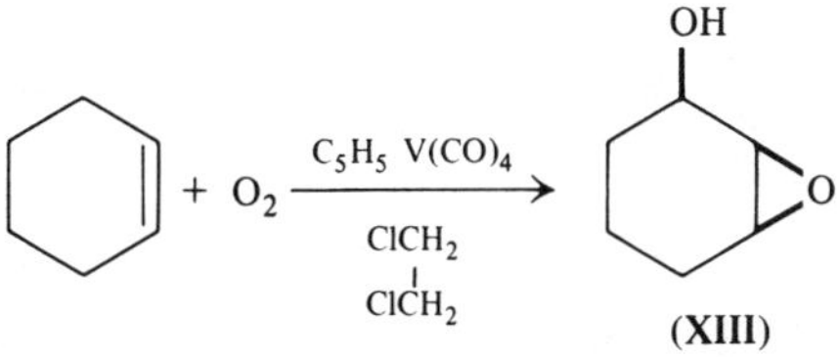

$$+ \quad O_2 \xrightarrow[\substack{ClCH_2 \\ | \\ ClCH_2}]{C_5H_5 \ V(CO)_4}$$

(XIII)

tion of terminal alkenes in the presence of catalytic amounts of hydrido-carbonyltris(triphenylphosphine)rhodium or tris(triphenylphosphine)chlororhodium affords methyl ketones (Dudley *et al.*, 1974).

Diphenylacetylene is oxidized by *tert*-butyl hydroperoxide and $Mo(CO)_6$ to give benzil (35%), benzoic acid (31%), and *tert*-butyl benzoate (11%) (Matlin and Sammes, 1973).

B. π-Allyl Complexes

Steroidal π-allyl complexes can be oxidatively cleaved to allyl alcohols with high stereoselectivity (Jones and Knox, 1975b). For example, the π-allyl palladium chloride dimer, **XIV**, derived from cholest-4-ene, undergoes bridge cleavage by pyridine and then oxidation by *m*-chloroperbenzoic acid to give **XVI** as the sole product. Similar reaction of the isomeric π-allyl

complex **XV** affords **XVII** in 61% yield and **XVIII** in 6% yield. These results suggest that the hydroxy group becomes preferentially attached to the same diastereotopic face of the π-allyl system as that which palladium previously occupied. Use of Collins reagent as the oxidizing agent results in the formation of α,β-unsaturated aldehydes (e.g., **XIX**) in moderate yields (Vedejs *et al.*, 1972). Ketones were obtained from σ,π-organopalladium compounds.

$$[(CH_3)_3CCH_2\!\!-\!\!\langle\!\!\langle\!\!-\!Pd\overset{Cl}{\underset{]_2}{\diagdown}} \xrightarrow[CH_2Cl_2]{CrO_3\cdot 2pyr} (CH_3)_3CCH_2\overset{CHO}{\underset{|}{C}}\!\!=\!\!CH_2$$

(XIX), 40%

C. Alcohols

Ruthenium carbonyl and dichlorotris(triphenylphosphine)ruthenium are effective catalysts for the oxidation of alcohols to aldehydes or ketones by *N*-methylmorpholine-*N*-oxide (Sharpless *et al.*, 1976).

$$n-C_{11}H_{23}CH_2OH + \quad\boxed{}\quad \xrightarrow[HCON(CH_3)_2]{Ru_3(CO)_{12}} n-C_{11}H_{23}CHO$$

80%

D. Ketones

The oxidation of ketones to acids can be catalyzed by $Rh_6(CO)_{16}$ (Mercer *et al.*, 1975, 1977).

$$\bigcirc\!\!=\!\!O + O_2 \xrightarrow{Rh_6(CO)_{16}} \overset{COOH}{\underset{\underset{COOH}{|}}{\underset{(CH_2)_4}{|}}}$$

E. Nitrogen Containing Compounds

Ozonide (Smetana, 1972) and *tert*-butyl or *tert*-amyl hydroperoxide (Sheng and Zajacek, 1968b; Tolstikov *et al.*, 1971a,c) are good reagents for converting tertiary amines into the corresponding amine oxides in the presence of $Mo(CO)_6$, $MoCl_5$, or $VO(acac)_2$. Molybdenum hexacarbonyl, $W(CO)_6$, and $[C_5H_5Mo(CO)_3]_2$ are quite ineffective catalysts in the *tert*-butyl hydroperoxide oxidation of aniline to nitrobenzene (Howe and Hiatt, 1970).

Nitroalkanes and nitrocycloalkanes are convertible to ketones by potassium *tert*-butoxide and *tert*-butyl hydroperoxide in the presence of molybdenum hexacarbonyl or vanadium oxyacetylacetonate (Bartlett *et al.*, 1977). Ketone, acetal, and ester functions are unaffected.

Oxaziridines can be synthesized in good yields from Schiff bases, a

$$\underset{\underset{NO_2}{|}}{CH_3\overset{\overset{O}{\|}}{C}CH_2CH_2CHCH_2CH_3} \quad + \quad K^{\oplus}\ominus OC(CH_3)_3 \quad + \quad (CH_3)_3C-OOH$$

$$\xrightarrow[\text{Mo(CO)}_6]{\quad 80°, 60\% \quad}$$

$$CH_3\overset{\overset{O}{\|}}{C}CH_2CH_2\underset{\underset{O}{\|}}{C}CH_2CH_3$$

hydroperoxide, and a molybdenum catalyst (Tolstikov *et al.*, 1971c). Azo compounds afford azoxy compounds in good yields under similar reaction conditions (Johnson and Gould, 1974).

$$CH_3O-\langle\text{benzene ring}\rangle-N=NPh \xrightarrow[\substack{(CH_3)_3C-OOH\\C_6H_6}]{Mo(CO)_6}$$

$$CH_3O-\langle\text{benzene ring}\rangle-\overset{\overset{O}{\|}}{N}=NPh \quad + \quad CH_3O-\langle\text{benzene ring}\rangle-N=\overset{\overset{O}{\|}}{N}Ph$$

53 : 47 (88% Yield)

F. Sulfides

Treatment of a sulfide with an equimolar quantity of *tert*-amyl hydroperoxide and a catalytic amount of Mo(CO)$_6$ or MoCl$_5$ affords sulfoxides in high yields. Use of 2 to 3 equivalents of the oxidizing agent results in conversion of the sulfide to the sulfone (Tolstikov *et al.*, 1972).

$$\langle\text{bicyclic structure}\rangle \quad + \quad \underset{\underset{CH_3}{|}}{C_2H_5\overset{\overset{CH_3}{|}}{C}-OOH} \xrightarrow[\substack{60°, 0.5\ hr\\quantitative}]{Mo(CO)_6} \langle\text{bicyclic structure}\rangle$$

II. REDUCTION

A. Aromatic Hydrocarbons

The reduction of olefins and alkynes by hydrogen and a transition metal organometallic catalyst will not be reviewed as it has been the subject of a recent book as well as several reviews (references in Birch, Volume 1; also Kagan, 1975). By contrast, the organometallic induced homogeneous reduction of aromatic hydrocarbons has only been studied in the past several years.

Tris(trimethylphosphite)π-allylcobalt is an excellent catalyst for the hydrogenation of aromatic to saturated hydrocarbons under mild conditions (Muetterties and Hirsekorn, 1974). Benzene undergoes hydrogenation three to four times faster than cyclohexene (Hirsekorn et al., 1975), but 1-hexene hydrogenates at a competitive rate (Rakowski et al., 1976). The catalyst displays remarkable stereoselectivity as reduction of benzene-d_6 gives all-cis-cyclohexane-d_6 (Muetterties et al., 1975). Cis selectivity was also observed using $[(C_5Me_5)RhCl_2]_2$ as the catalyst (Russell et al., 1977).

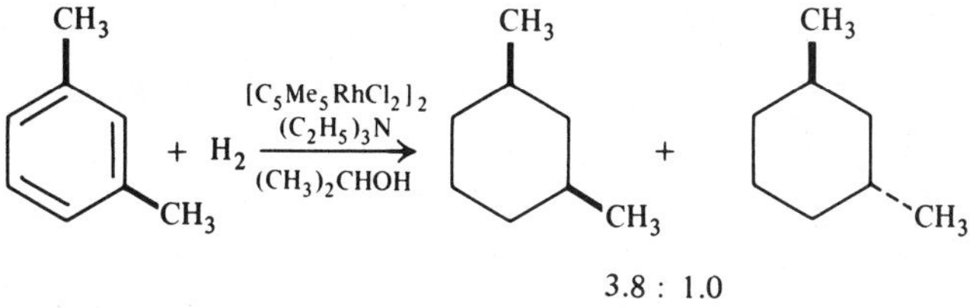

3.8 : 1.0

Polycyclic aromatic hydrocarbons undergo hydrogenation to dihydro derivatives (e.g., anthracene to 9,10-dihydroanthracene) under oxo conditions $[Co_2(CO)_8, CO, H_2]$ (Friedman et al., 1959; Wender et al., 1950, 1951). The results can best be accounted for on the basis of free radical intermediates (Feder and Halpern, 1975).

B. π-Allyl and σ,π-Complexes

Treatment of steroidal π-allylpalladium chloride dimers (e.g., XX) with lithium aluminum hydride affords olefins (e.g., cholest-5-ene XXI) of retained configuration (Jones and Knox, 1975a).

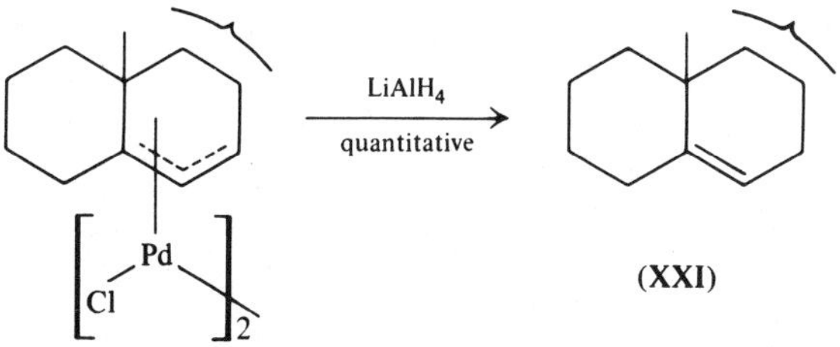

(XX)   (XXI)

The σ,π-complex **XXIII**, obtained by treatment of **XXII** with bis(benzo-nitrile)palladium dichloride, is reductively cleaved by sodium borohydride under gentle conditions to give 4-chlorocyclooctene **(XXIV)** in 67% yield (Albelo *et al.*, 1975).

C. Halides

Several useful organometallic reagents have been developed for converting halides to hydrocarbons. Alkyl, allyl, and benzyl halides can be dehalogenated to hydrocarbons in reasonable yields using *cis*-hydridotetracarbonyl(triphenylphosphine)manganese in toluene, but the reaction is slow (Booth and Shaw, 1972). The same conversion can be achieved with LiCu(H)R (R = alkyl, alkynyl), generated *in situ* from copper hydride and the appropriate organolithium compound (Masamune *et al.*, 1974). The above noted halides, as well as α-halo ketones or vinyl halides, can be dehalogenated in a highly stereoselective fashion (e.g., **XXV** → **XXVI**) using the hydridotetracarbonylferrate anion, formed from iron pentacarbonyl and potassium hydroxide (Alper, 1975a). This reagent may react with a halide by initial S_N2 displacement, followed by cis-elimination of an octahedral iron intermediate, or by a radical pathway. This reaction has also been applied to the conversion of acid chlorides to aldehydes (Cole and Pettit, 1977).

Lithium dimethylcuprate can reduce α-acetoxy and α-bromo ketones, provided brief reaction times are used (Bull and Tuinman, 1973). A similar

type of reaction has been reported for α,α-dichloroesters and lactones (Villeras *et al.*, 1973). Treatment of polyhalogenomethyls with $Ni(CO)_4$ in

tetrahydrofuran results in reduction to mono- or dihalogenomethyls. This reaction has been applied to the stereoselective synthesis of sugar derivatives. Monohalides are unaffected as illustrated in the partial dehalogenation of the trichloromethyl group of **XXVII** to **XXVIII** in the presence of bromine (Kunieda *et al.*, 1972; Tamura *et al.*, 1972).

(XXVII)   (XXVIII)

Aryl, alkyl, and vinyl halides can be reduced to hydrocarbons by the use of dicyclopentadienyl titanium dichloride and magnesium (Nelson and Tufariello, 1975) or isopropylmagnesium bromide (Colomer and Corriu, 1975).

The reagent system of $TiCl_3 \cdot 3THF$ and magnesium is also useful for effecting this type of dehalogenation (Tyrlik and Wolochowicz, 1975).

D. Epoxides

Reaction of the cyclopentadienyliron dicarbonyl anion, readily prepared from commercially available cyclopentadienyliron dicarbonyl dimer and sodium amalgam, with epoxides gives olefin complexes **(XXXI)** in good yields. The olefin ligand can be liberated from the complex using iodide ion (Giering et al., 1972). The reaction occurs with net retention of configuration and was proposed to occur via intermediates **XXIX** and **XXX**.

A cyclic intermediate, formed by intramolecular attack of O^- at a terminal carbonyl carbon of **XXIX**, should also be considered.

If the intermediate alkoxide **XXIX** is thermally decomposed (reflux in THF or heat at $130°-240°$), then collapse to the olefin occurs but with inversion of configuration with respect to the reactant epoxide (Rosenblum *et al.*, 1975). This inversion process is useful for dialkyl or diaryl epoxides, but α,β-epoxy carbonyl compounds give mixtures of cis and trans olefins.

To complement the Fp⁻ results, Dowd and Kang (1974) found that dicobalt octacarbonyl can deoxygenate α,β-epoxy diesters such as **XXXII** to olefins with inversion of configuration. Simpler epoxides (e.g., dialkyl) undergo rearrangement rather than deoxygenation by Co₂(CO)₈ (Eisenmann, 1962).

(XXXII)

If steroidal α,β-epoxy ketones are exposed to two equivalents of lithium dimethylcuprate in ether at 0° for a short time (5 min), then reduction, rather

than alkylation, is the major reaction process (Bull and Lachmann, 1973). Reduction is a secondary pathway in the reaction of simple epoxides with the cuprate reagent (Johnson *et al.*, 1973).

E. Saturated and α,β-Unsaturated Ketones

Ketones are generally alkylated by lithium dialkylcuprates. However, $(n\text{-}C_4H_9)_2CuLi$ reduces pericyclocamphor to the corresponding alcohol in 70% yield. Alkylation does occur using $(CH_3)_2CuLi$. It is not apparent why the two cuprates react in a different manner towards the strained ketone (Scott and Cotton, 1973).

The cuprate $LiCu(H)R$ (R = alkyl, alkynyl) can reduce aldehydes or ketones to alcohols in good yields. The double bond of α,β-unsaturated ketones is reduced by this reagent. The ester function is unaffected (Masamune et al., 1974). Other reagents which have been employed for these double bond

85% (7:3 cis:trans)

reductions include $HFe(CO)_4^-$ (Noyori et al., 1972; Wada and Matsuda, 1973), $HFe_2(CO)_8^-$ (Collman et al., 1978), $HCr_2(CO)_{10}^-$ (Boldrini et al., 1976), and carbon dioxide and water catalyzed "by free" (Kitamura et al., 1973), or better, resin supported (Kitamura et al., 1975) rhodium carbonyl. Mixtures of lithium aluminum hydride and either copper iodide or titanium trichloride are also highly effective reagent combinations (Ashby et al., 1976).

The hydridotetracarbonylferrate anion effects both double bond reduction and deacylation of α,β-unsaturated dicarbonyls to alkyl methyl ketones (Yamashita et al., 1975).

F. Anhydrides

Disodium tetracarbonylferrate can convert simple anhydrides to aldehydic acids under mild conditions (Watanabe et al., 1973). Carboxylic alkylcarbonic anhydrides react with $Na_2Fe(CO)_4$ to give moderate amounts of aldehydes (Watanabe et al., 1975).

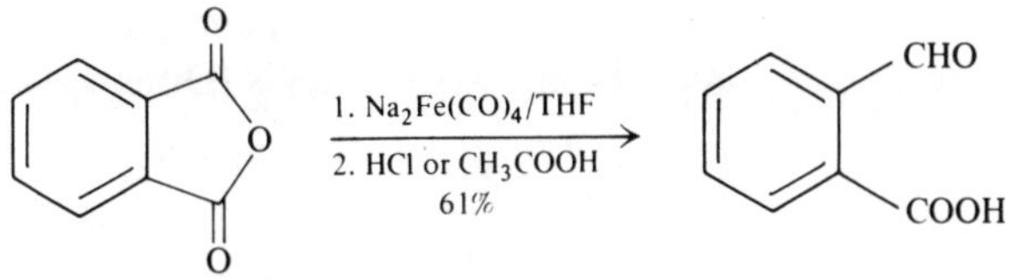

G. Schiff Bases, Diazines, and Enamines

Reaction of triiron dodecacarbonyl with methanol affords the hydridoundecacarbonyltriferrate anion $[HFe_3(CO)_{11}{}^-]$ which is a convenient reagent for reducing the carbon–nitrogen double bond of Schiff bases and diazines such as phthalazine (Alper, 1972a, 1973a). It is particularly useful for hetero-

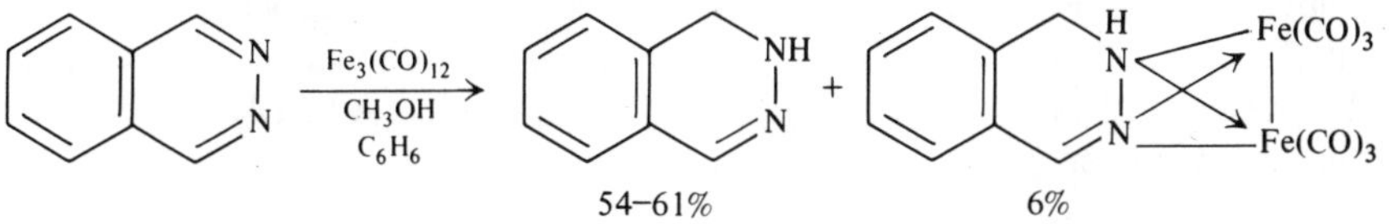

54–61%   6%

cyclic systems where other reagents (e.g., $LiAlH_4$) either fail to effect reduction or give mixtures of products. The $HFe(CO)_4{}^-$ anion can effect the same transformation (H. Alper, unpublished).

Reduction of enamines to saturated amines can be attained using the hydridoironcarbonyl anions $HFe(CO)_4{}^-$, $HFe_2(CO)_8{}^-$, or $HFe_3(CO)_{11}{}^-$ (Mitsudo et al., 1975).

H. Oximes, Benzohydroxamoyl Chlorides

Iron pentacarbonyl can regenerate carbonyl compounds from oximes under aprotic conditions (Alper and Edward, 1967). The presence of boron trifluoride etherate affords products in 55–81% yields although the reaction can take place—sometimes in reduced yields—in the absence of the Lewis acid (XXXIII → XXXIV) (Alper and Edward, 1969). The intermediate was isolated using the sterically hindered reactant, methyl mesityl ketoxime (Dondoni and Barbaro, 1975).

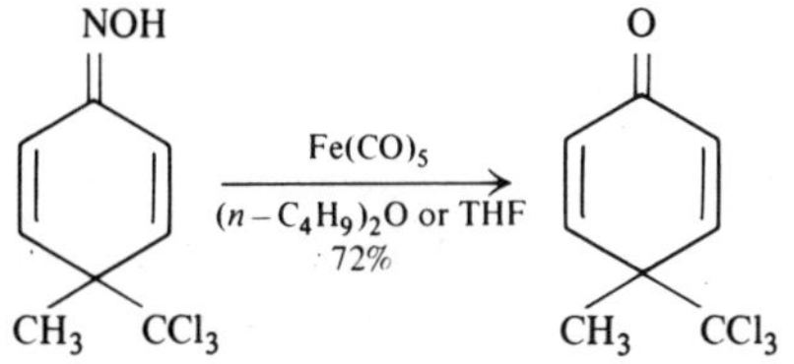

(XXXIII)   (XXXIV)

Amide oximes react with one or more equivalents of $Fe(CO)_5$ in hot tetrahydrofuran to give amidines in 70–90% yields (Dondoni and Barbaro,

$$\underset{X}{R-C=NOH} \xrightarrow[\substack{\Delta \\ THF}]{Fe(CO)_5} \underset{X}{R-C=NH}$$

$$X = NHPh,\ N(CH_3)_2,\ N(CH_3)Ph,\ NHC_6H_4Cl\text{-}p$$
$$R = Ph,\quad p\text{-}NO_2C_6H_4,\quad 2,4,6\text{-}(CH_3)_3C_6H_2$$

1975). This deoxygenation process is probably similar to that for simple oximes.

Nitriles are formed in 33–76% yields by reaction of benzohydroxamoyl chlorides with $Fe(CO)_5$ in THF (Genco et al., 1973). Superior yields of nitriles resulted by use of the $HFe_3(CO)_{11}^-$ ion. The reaction can occur in the presence of NO_2, Cl, F, NH_2, and OCH_3 groups. A nitrile oxide intermediate has been proposed for the $Fe(CO)_5$ reaction.

I. N-Oxides, Nitrones, Azo, Azoxy Compounds, and Nitroxyl Radicals

Iron pentacarbonyl is a useful reagent for deoxygenating aliphatic, aromatic, and heterocyclic N-oxides (Alper and Edward, 1970). The reaction occurs in the presence of olefin, lactam, and alkoxy functionalities as well as water (as a hydrate). Azoxybenzenes can be reduced to azo compounds, and nitrones to Schiff bases, using this reagent. These reactions may take place by nucleophilic attack of the oxide at a terminal carbonyl carbon to give a dipolar intermediate (XXXV), which can then collapse to the deoxygenated

product. Support for this mechanism is provided by the isolation of an intermediate compound of type XXXV in the decomplexation of a diene-iron carbonyl complex with trimethylamine oxide (Eekhof et al., 1976), and isolation of $(CH_3)_3NFe(CO)_4$ in the low temperature reaction of $(CH_3)_3NO$ with $Fe(CO)_5$ (Elzinga and Hogeveen, 1977).

The deoxygenation of azoxy to azobenzene by $Cr_2(CO)_{10}^{-2}$ has been noted (King and Harmon, 1975). Dicyclopentadienyltitanium dichloride and magnesium are a useful reagent combination for preparing hydrazo from azo compounds (Nelson and Tufariello, 1975). Nitroxyl radicals deoxygenate to amines upon treatment with $HFe_3(CO)_{11}^-$ (Alper, 1973b).

J. Nitro Compounds

Hydrogenation of nitroaromatics to aromatic amines can be catalyzed by $RuCl_2(PPh_3)_3$ or $Fe(CO)_3(PPh_3)_2$ (Knifton, 1976). The reaction can be effected at elevated temperatures in the presence of nitrile, ester, and hydroxy functional groups, amongst others. In addition, significant ortho-selectivity was observed for dinitroaromatics. This reduction process has also been applied to 1-nitrododecane (Knifton, 1975).

Amines can also be synthesized by treatment of nitrobenzenes with the *in situ* generated hydridoundecacarbonyltriferrate anion in refluxing benzene for 10–17 hr (Landesberg *et al.*, 1972). A superior way of effecting this transformation is by the use of phase transfer catalysis (des Abbayes and Alper, 1977). Reaction of nitrobenzenes such as *p*-chloronitrobenzene with half the molar quantity of $Fe_3(CO)_{12}$, aqueous sodium hydroxide, benzene,

and benzyltriethylammonium chloride or 18-crown-6 (Alper *et al.*, 1977a) as the catalyst (room temperature) affords anilines in 60–92% yields. The reduction can also be effected using $Fe(CO)_5$ or $Fe_2(CO)_9$ and aqueous sodium hydroxide in a two-phase system, but a catalyst is not required.

The reduction of nitrobenzene to aniline by carbon monoxide and water in the presence of rhodium catalysts [e.g., $Rh_6(CO)_{16}$] (Iqbal, 1975) or $Ru_3(CO)_{12}$ (L'Eplattenier *et al.*, 1970) has been described. Azo compounds were isolated by $Fe(CO)_5$-catalyzed reaction of nitroarenes with carbon monoxide at elevated temperatures and pressures (Kmiecik, 1965). Azo, azoxy compounds, amines, or diiron hexacarbonyl complexes were formed by reaction of nitroarenes with at at least an equimolar amount of $Fe(CO)_5$, the nature of the products depending on the reagent concentration (Alper and Edward, 1970). For instance, use of equimolar amounts of $Fe(CO)_5$ and nitrobenzene gave azoxybenzene in 64% yield and azobenzene was formed in 3% yield. The yield of the latter increased to 76% by use of a 1.5/1.0 mole ratio of metal carbonyl to nitro compound. Use of excess $Fe(CO)_5$, or better $Fe_2(CO)_9$ in THF, gave the diiron hexacarbonyl complex **(XXXVI)** in 52%

$$\text{1.5 } Fe(CO)_5/(n-C_4H_9)_2O$$

$$PhNO_2 \xrightarrow[(n-C_4H_9)_2O]{\text{1.0 } Fe(CO)_5} PhN{=\!=}NPh + PhN{=\!=}NPh$$

(with O below the first $PhN{=\!=}NPh$)

excess $Fe(CO)_5$
or $Fe_2(CO)_9$

C_6H_6 / $h\nu$

(XXXVII) — structure with NH_2 and $NHPh$ groups

$\xleftarrow[(C_2H_5)_2O]{LiAlH_4}$

(XXXVI) — benzimidazole structure with $Fe(CO)_3$, $Fe(CO)_3$, N–H and N–Ph

(XXXVII)   **(XXXVI)**

yield. Cleavage of **XXXVI** by lithium aluminum hydride affords the ortho-semidine **XXXVII**, thus permitting the reduction of a nitro group to an amine with concurrent ortho-substitution (Bagga et al., 1969; H. Alper and E. C. H. Keung, unpublished).

The presence of meta or para electron-donating substituents on the benzene ring gave fair to good yields of azo compounds on reaction with $Fe(CO)_5$ (1.4–1.7 equivalents), while azo compounds and/or amines were obtained when electron-attracting substituents were present on the ring (e.g., p-CN). ortho-Substituted nitrobenzenes, on similar treatment afford amines and/or azo compounds, or insertion products (Alper and Edward, 1970). Deoxygenation and cyclization of **XXXVIII** by $Fe(CO)_5$ gave 2-phenyl-2H-indazole **(XXXIX)** (Mohan, 1974).

Modest amounts of formamides and/or ureas resulted from reaction of aliphatic and cycloalkyl nitro compounds with $Fe(CO)_5$ (Alper, 1972b). Photoreduction of aromatic nitro compounds to nitroso compounds or

(XXXVIII)   (XXXIX)

isocyanates can be effected in fair yields in the presence of a variety of metal carbonyls [e.g., $Fe(CO)_5$, $Co_2(CO)_8$, $Mn_2(CO)_{10}$, $[C_5H_5Fe(CO)_2]_2$] (Onoda and Masai, 1974). Azo compounds can be conveniently prepared by treatment of nitrobenzenes with $Co_2(CO)_8$ or (benzene)tetracobalt nonacarbonyl in benzene (Alper and Paik, 1978).

K. C- and N-Nitroso Compounds

Azobenzenes can be synthesized in good yield by deoxygenative coupling of nitrosobenzenes using $Fe(CO)_5$ (Alper and Edward, 1970) or $Cr_2(CO)_{10}^{-2}$ (King and Harmon, 1975). Iron (Alper and Edward, 1970) or Group VI (Alper, 1971) metal carbonyls are good reagents for converting nitrosamines to secondary amines in ether solvents. Ureas are sometimes formed from nonaromatic nitrosamines.

L. Phosphine Oxides

Disproportionation complexes are formed by thermal reaction of either trialkyl or triarylphosphine oxides with $Fe(CO)_5$ in polar or nonpolar solvents (H. Alper and E. C. H. Keung, unpublished). Irradiation of Ph_3PO and $Fe(CO)_5$ at 80° gave similar products (Hieber and Lipp, 1959). Treatment of phosphineimines with $Fe(CO)_5$ in THF results in a unique deoxygenation of a carbonyl group of the metal carbonyl to give Ph_3PO and isonitrile complexes (Alper and Partis, 1972).

M. Sulfur Compounds

Iron pentacarbonyl is an excellent reagent for deoxygenating dialkyl, diaryl, or heterocyclic sulfoxides to sulfides (Alper and Keung, 1970). The mechanism for this reaction is similar to that described for the N-oxide–$Fe(CO)_5$ reaction. Moderate yields of thiobenzophenones were realized by reaction of diaryl sulfines with $Fe_2(CO)_9$ in benzene or $Mn_2(CO)_{10}$ in heptane (Alper, 1975b).

α-Bromo sulfoxides (XL) react with $Mo(CO)_6$ in 1,2-dimethoxyethane to give thioacetals **(XLIII)** in good yields, accompanied by *gem*-dihalides. This reaction may occur via initial deoxygenation of the sulfoxide function, the resultant α-bromo sulfide **(XLI)** being converted to the thioacetal by a catalytic amount of the metal carbonyl (via **XLII**) (Alper and Wall, 1976).

$$RSOCH_2Br \xrightarrow{Mo(CO)_6} RSCH_2Br \xrightarrow{Mo(CO)_6 \ cat} RSCH_2 - Br$$

(XL)   (XLI)   Mo   RS
                                                                      (CO)$_5$ |
                                                                                       CH$_2$Br

                    (XLI)   (XLII)

                                                         ↓

CH$_2$Br$_2$ +   RSCH$_2$SR ←———— RSCH$_2$ – $\overset{\oplus}{S}$–R
                          ↓   ↓   CH$_2$Br
                         Mo   (CO)$_5$Mo
                        (CO)$_5$ Br$^{\ominus}$

                          ↓ (XLI)

              RSCH$_2$SR + (XLII)

                    (XLIII)

Sulfonyl chlorides react with a 1:1 mixture of $Fe(CO)_5$ and BF_3 etherate, in a dipolar aprotic solvent such as *N,N*-dimethylacetamide, to give thiolsulfonates in 36–71% yield (Alper, 1969b). This deoxygenation and coupling reaction probably occurs via initial oxidative addition (Alper and Keung, 1972).

Good yields of disulfides were obtained by treatment of sulfonyl chlorides with $Mo(CO)_6$ (Alper, 1969a), or sulfenyl halides with iron, chromium, or nickel carbonyls (Lindner and Vitzthum, 1969). Decomposition of sulfonyl azides by $Fe(CO)_5$ or $Fe_2(CO)_9$ affords sulfonamides in low yields (Abramovitch *et al.*, 1974).

III. ADDITION AND CONDENSATION REACTIONS

A. Olefins

Hydrozirconation of olefins can be readily accomplished by the use of the hydride **XLIV** derived from the relatively inexpensive reagent, dicyclopentadienylzirconium dichloride (Hart and Schwartz, 1974). Very

$$(\pi-C_5H_5)_2ZrCl_2 \xrightarrow{\ H^-\ } (\pi-C_5H_5)_2Zr\begin{smallmatrix}H\\\\Cl\end{smallmatrix} \xrightarrow[\text{or cis- or trans-}\atop\text{4-octane}]{n-C_6H_{13}CH=CH_2} (\pi-C_5H_5)_2Zr\begin{smallmatrix}n-C_8H_{17}\\\\Cl\end{smallmatrix}$$

(XLIV)   (XLV)

rapid isomerization of internal to terminal alkyl zirconium chlorides occurs under mild conditions. For example, reaction of **XLIV** with 1-octene or *cis*- or *trans*-4-octene gives the *n*-octyl zirconium chloride **XLV**. The carbon–zirconium σ-bond can be cleaved by electrophiles such as H^+ and bromine (Labinger *et al.*, 1975) and by oxidizing agents including oxygen, hydrogen peroxide, and *tert*-butyl hydroperoxide (Blackburn *et al.*, 1975). Electrophilic cleavage by bromine occurs with retention of configuration. Carbonyl insertion has also been described (Bertelo and Schwartz, 1975).

$$n-C_8H_{17}Br \xleftarrow[96\%]{Br_2} (\mathbf{XLV}) \xrightarrow[100\%]{H^+} n-C_8H_{18}$$

$$\Bigg\downarrow {\scriptstyle O_2 \atop \text{then } H_3O^+}\ \ 57\%$$

$$n-C_8H_{17}OH$$

While boron, aluminum, and other hydrides dimetalate 1,3-dienes, **XLIV** undergoes 1,2-addition to the least substituted double bond, and subsequent carbonylation and hydrolysis affords γ,δ-unsaturated aldehydes in good yields (Bertelo and Schwartz, 1976).

The $Fe(CO)_5$-catalyzed addition and telomerization reactions of olefins with polyhalogenomethyl compounds has been investigated in considerable

$$ClCH_2CH_2CCl_3 \; + \; CH_2 = CH_2 \; \xrightarrow[\substack{135°, \; 46 \; atm \\ 77\%}]{Fe(CO)_5, \; (CH_3)_2CHOH} \; ClCH_2CH_2\overset{\overset{\displaystyle Cl}{|}}{\underset{\underset{\displaystyle Cl}{|}}{C}}CH_2CH_2Cl$$

detail (Friedlina and Chukovskaya, 1974; Velichko and Vinogradova, 1975; Friedlina and Velichko, 1977). The reaction has also been applied to vinyl halides, esters, and nitriles, as well as to allyl chlorides and simple olefins. Ferrous chloride, $Co_2(CO)_8$ and $Cr(CO)_6$, are also useful catalysts. Lac-

$$CH_3(CH_2)_3CH = CH_2 \; + \; Cl_3C\underset{\underset{\displaystyle O}{\|}}{C}OCH_3 \; \xrightarrow[\substack{150° \\ 74\%}]{Co_2(CO)_8} \; CH_3(CH_2)_3\overset{\overset{\displaystyle Cl}{|}}{C}HCH_2\overset{\overset{\displaystyle Cl}{|}}{\underset{\underset{\displaystyle Cl}{|}}{C}} - COOCH_3$$

tones are the major products when $[C_5H_5Fe(CO)_2]_2$ or $[C_5H_5Mo(CO)_3]_2$ are employed as catalysts (Mori and Tsuji, 1972).

The organic halide–ethylene growth reaction can be catalyzed by $Ru(CO)_3$ $(PPh_3)_2$ (Magoon et al., 1975).

Aminomethylation of olefins can be attained in good yields by reaction of alkenes with secondary amines, carbon monoxide, and water in the presence of Rh_2O_3 and/or $Fe(CO)_5$. Rhodium oxide is superior to $Fe(CO)_5$ but highest yields can be realized when they are used together. This reaction has been applied to the synthesis of long-chain alkylamines (Iqbal, 1975).

Thiols add to olefins in the presence of $Fe(CO)_5$ to give sulfides (Nesmeyanov *et al.*, 1962).

An interesting, and potentially useful, approach to the synthesis of optically active cyclopropanes is by the use of chiral iron complexes **(XLVI)** as methylene transfer agents to olefins (Davison *et al.*, 1974). Reaction of **XLVI** with 1-phenyl-1-propene under acidic conditions affords $(-)$-$(1R,2R)$ *trans*-2-methylphenylcyclopropane (26% enantiomeric excess).

B. Alkynes

Hydrozirconation of alkynes, followed by halogenation with *N*-halosuccinimide (*N*-bromo, *N*-chloro) affords vinyl halides in reasonable yields (Hart *et al.*, 1975). Vinyl cuprates, obtained by stereospecific addition of alkylcoppers to terminal alkynes, react with iodine in ether at $-30°$ to give vinyl iodides (Normant *et al.*, 1974).

C. π-Allyl Complexes

Allylamines can be synthesized in good yield by treatment of π-allyl palladium chloride complexes with amines (Akermark and Zetterberg, 1975). Highest yields and fastest reactions occurred when a coordinating ligand such as tri-*n*-butylphosphine was present. In the example given, the reaction is stereospecific (*E*-olefin), but in some instances small quantities of the *Z*-isomer were isolated, as well as an isomeric allylamine.

144   HOWARD ALPER

D. Aldehydes and Ketones

Aromatic aldehydes can be converted to esters in the presence of a catalytic amount of disodium tetracarbonylferrate (Yamashita *et al.*, 1976).

Pentacarbonylchromate $[Cr(CO)_5^{-2}]$ or the iron hydride, $HFe(CO)_4^-$, can induce alkylation and arylation of carbonyl compounds and active methylene compounds by aldehydes (Cainelli *et al.*, 1973, 1975). The iron

hydride may catalyze condensation of the carbonyl compound to form an α,β-unsaturated carbonyl which is known to undergo hydrogenation by the hydride (Noyori *et al.*, 1972). Related reductive amination reactions using $HFe(CO)_4^-$ (Watanabe *et al.*, 1974a,b, 1976a; Boldrini *et al.*, 1974a), $Rh_6(CO)_{16}$, or $Co_2(CO)_8$ (Marko and Bakos, 1974) have also been de-

scribed. 3-Substituted indoles can be synthesized by the reductive alkylation process (Boldrini *et al.*, 1974b).

Rhodium carbonyl is an effective catalyst for the condensation of aromatic aldehydes and nitro compounds (CO, pressure) to Schiff bases (Iqbal, *ca.* 65%

1972a). The reaction proceeds further for *o*-phthalaldehyde to give N-substituted isoindolones (Iqbal, 1972b). It has been proposed that initial

deoxygenation of the nitroarene takes place to give a nitrene, free or complexed, which subsequently reacts with the carbonyl compound. Schiff bases can also be obtained in 90–100% yields by cobalt carbonyl [Fe(CO)$_5$ and Group VI metal carbonyls are less effective] catalyzed condensation of aldehydes with isocyanates (Drapier *et al.*, 1972).

Acetalization of crotonaldehyde was reported to occur at 25° using chlorodicarbonylrhodium(I) dimer as the catalyst (Hoffman, 1974) while much more drastic conditions (50°–200°, 10–200 atm CO) are required for the cobalt carbonyl catalyzed acetalization of aliphatic aldehydes (Katsnel'son *et al.*, 1973).

E. Isonitriles and Isocyanates

Treatment of isonitriles with azides in the presence of Fe(CO)$_5$ at 90° affords carbodiimides in reasonable yields (Saegusa *et al.*, 1970).

Cobalt carbonyl is a good catalyst for the reaction of anhydrides with

$$(RCO)_2O + PhNCO \xrightarrow{Co_2(CO)_8} PhN(COR)_2 + CO_2$$

isocyanates to give imines (Drapier *et al.*, 1973). The reaction occurs, albeit at a much reduced rate, in the absence of a catalyst.

Phenylisocyanate undergoes cyclocondensation with *N*-sulfinylaniline in the presence of Fe(CO)$_5$ or Co$_2$(CO)$_8$ to give dioxo-1,2,4-triazolidine (Drapier *et al.*, 1975).

$$PhNSO + PhNCO \xrightarrow{Co_2(CO)_8} \text{[structure]} + PhN=NPh$$

16%   20%

IV. ELIMINATION PROCESSES

A. Dehydrogenation

Steroidal α,β-unsaturated ketones can be dehydrogenated, via π-allyl complexes, to give conjugated dienones. Decomposition of the π-allyl complex can be effected either thermally (Howsam and McQuillin, 1968) or by treatment with diethyl malonate anion or cyanide ion (Harrison et al., 1969).

B. Dehalogenation

Dehalogenation of 1,2-dibromoalkanes to olefins can be effected under mild conditions using lithium dimethyl or di-n-butyl cuprate (Posner and Ting, 1973). Although the reaction is not stereospecific, it has the advantage in that it can tolerate functional groups such as the carbalkoxy function.

$$BrCH_2CH(CH_2)_8COOCH_3 \xrightarrow[\substack{(C_2H_5)_2O \\ -20°, 90\%}]{5(n-C_4H_9)_2CuLi} \text{[CH}_2\text{=CH]}(CH_2)_8COOCH_3$$

with Br below the first carbon.

Titanocene can also induce debromination of 1,2-dibromoalkanes at room temperature (Merijanian et al., 1972). Coupling products were isolated in several instances. Interestingly, diphenylacetylene was obtained from trans-1,2-dibromo or trans-1,2-diiodostilbene.

C. Decarbonylation

The subject was reviewed by Tsuji and Ohno (1969).

Wilkinson's catalyst and chlorocarbonylbis(triphenylphosphine)rhodium [or iridium] can catalyze the thermal decarbonylation of aromatic acid halides to aryl halides. An intermediate Rh(III) hydride is involved in the reaction (Suggs, 1978). For aliphatic acid halides, subsequent elimination of HX frequently occurs from the generated alkyl halide (Ohno and Tsuji, 1968; Blum et al., 1967, 1971; Strohmeier and Pfohler, 1976).

$$n-C_7H_{15}\overset{\overset{\displaystyle O}{\|}}{C}Br \xrightarrow[\substack{200°,\ 1\ hr \\ 90\%\ yield}]{(Ph_3P)_2Rh(CO)Cl} n-C_5H_{11}CH{=}CH_2 + \underset{CH_3}{\diagup\!\!\diagdown} + \underset{C_4H_9}{\diagup\!\!\diagdown}\!\!-C_4H_9$$

$$71:24:5$$

Wilkinson's catalyst is useful for effecting intramolecular decarbonylation of aldehydes to hydrocarbons with retention of configuration (Walborsky and Allen, 1971). Decarbonylation of disubstituted cyclopropenones by iron, nickel, or cobalt carbonyls results in the formation of alkynes (Bird and Hudec, 1959). Tetraphenylethylene was obtained in 68% yield by reaction of diphenylketene with cobalt carbonyl (Hong et al., 1968).

D. Desulfonation

The desulfonation of aromatic sulfonyl halides to aromatic halides can be catalyzed by platinum metal complexes [e.g., $Rh(CO)Cl(PPh_3)_2$] (Blum and Scharf, 1970).

E. Desulfurization

Stereoselective desulfurization of episulfides (thiiranes) can be achieved by using $Fe_2(CO)_9$ at 80° (Trost and Ziman, 1973) or 15° (H. Alper and B. D. Sash, unpublished), or by use of hydridopentacarbonylmanganese (Beck et al., 1973). Bis(triphenylphosphine)nickel dicarbonyl can catalyze elimination of thioanhydrides (e.g., XLVII, X = S), or anhydrides, to olefins. Diiron

$$\underset{Ph}{\overset{S}{\triangle}}\!\!-Ph \xrightarrow[15°]{Fe_2(CO)_9} \underset{Ph}{\overset{Ph}{\diagup\!\!=\!\!\diagdown}} + S_2Fe_2(CO)_6 + S_2Fe_3(CO)_9$$

$$78\%$$

enneacarbonyl or Wilkinson's catalyst could also be used for **XLVII**, X = S (Trost and Chen, 1971).

(XLVII)   X = S, 56%; X = O, 53%

Bis(1,5-cyclooctadiene)nickel is a good reagent for the stereospecific desulfurization of thionocarbonates to olefins (Semmelhack and Stauffer, 1973).

The same transformation can be realized, but nonstereospecifically, using $Fe(CO)_5$ (Daub *et al.*, 1972, 1974).

Treatment of thioketones and thionamides with $HFe(CO)_4^-$ gives hydrocarbons and amines, respectively (Alper, 1975c). Tetraarylethylenes were

formed from thiones and $Co_2(CO)_8$ (Alper and Paik, 1977) or $Mn_2(CO)_{10}$ (Alper, 1974).

Thiolactams react with $Fe(CO)_5$ in THF to give cyclic Schiff bases (H. Alper, unpublished). Nitriles are obtained from thioamides or amides (Alper and Edward, 1968).

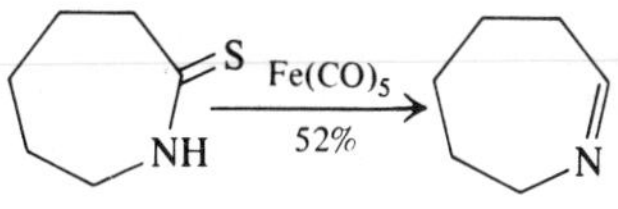

F. Nitrogen

Iron or molybdenum carbonyls react with α-diazo ketones to give unsaturated carbonyls (Matlin and Sammes, 1973).

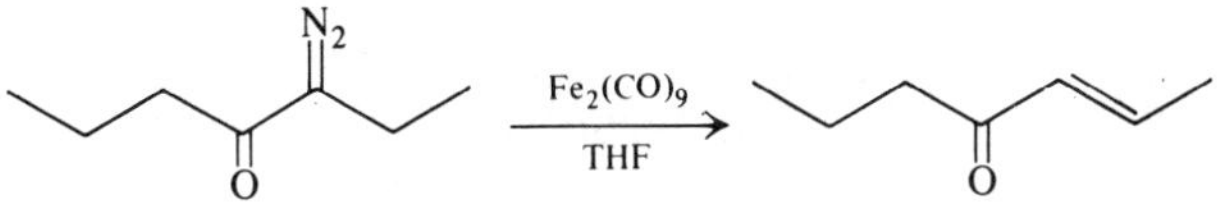

cis : trans (82 : 13)

V. CLEAVAGE REACTIONS

The allyloxycarbonyl function is a good protecting group for amines and alcohols. Removal of the protecting group can be accomplished in high yield using $Ni(CO)_4$ in $HCON(CH_3)_2$ (Corey and Suggs, 1973).

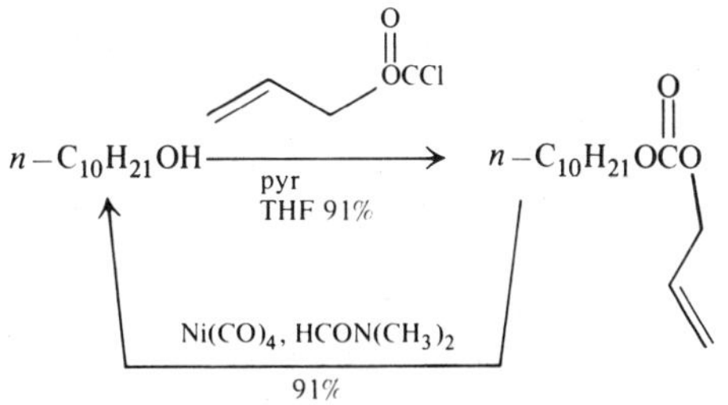

Group VI metal carbonyls catalyze the thermal or photochemical reaction of acyclic and cyclic ethers with acid halides to give esters (e.g., 4-chloropentylacetate, **XLVIII**) in good yields (Alper and Huang, 1973). The order of effectiveness for $M(CO)_6$ is Mo > W > Cr. Group V substituted

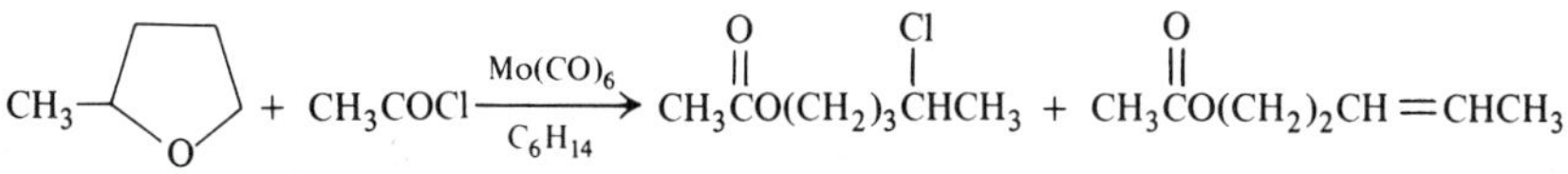

(**XLVIII**), 80%　　　　　7%

derivatives are also good catalysts [e.g., $(Ph_3P)Mo(CO)_5$]. The reaction occurs with inversion or retention (partial or complete) of configuration, depending on the ether used. An ionic mechanism is likely for this reaction.

Aryl and thiolic esters react with disodium tetracarbonylferrate to give aldehydes in moderate yields. However, long reaction times are required, and the reaction is not applicable to alkyl esters (Watanabe et al., 1976b).

VI. REARRANGEMENTS

Certain organometallics and inorganic compounds catalyze the rearrangement of strained ring systems under gentle conditions (Bishop, 1976). Several fascinating and useful reactions have been described, but it must be pointed out that most of the reported yields in this area are vapor phase chromatographic or nuclear magnetic resonance rather than isolated yields.

A. Polycyclic Compounds

Rhodium(I) complexes are excellent catalysts for the conversion of cubanes to syn-tricyclooctadienes (Cassar et al., 1970a). The rearrangement of bishomocubane derivatives by different metal complexes has also been described (Dauben and Kielbania, 1971; Takaya et al., 1973; Paquette et al., 1975a,b). Of particular note is the conversion of the 1,8-bishomocubanes **(XLIX)** to dienes **(L)** and the snoutane ring system **(LI)**. The proportion of

	(L)	(LI)
$R_1 = R_2 = H$	99.5%	0.5%
$R_1 = CH_3, R_2 = H$	92.3%	7.7%
$R_1 = R_2 = CH_3$	72.5%	27.5%

LI increases with successive replacement of methyl for hydrogen in R_1 and R_2. Steric effects are significant in these reactions. Much greater amounts of snoutane derivatives are formed with palladium(II) catalysts.

Snoutene, formed by $[Rh(CO)_2Cl]_2$-promoted rearrangement of diademane (de Meijere, 1974), undergoes further rearrangement at 60° in the presence of the rhodium(I) complex (de Meijere and Meyer, 1974). Cunaene is converted to semibullvalene by $[Rh(norbornadiene)Cl]_2$ (Cassar et al., 1970b).

Quadricyclanes (e.g., **LII**) are converted to norbornadienes **(LIII)** by exposure to nickel(0) [e.g., bis(1,5-cyclooctadiene)nickel] (Noyori et al., 1975), rhodium(I) [e.g., $[Rh(CO)_2Cl]_2$] (Hogeveen and Volger, 1967a; Cassar and Halpern, 1970; Hogeveen and Nusse, 1973, 1974), platinum(II) [e.g., (norbornadiene)PtCl$_2$], and palladium(II) (Hogeveen and Volger, 1967a)

complexes. In the Ni(O) reaction, a mechanism involving initial edgewise coordination of quadricyclane to the metal **LIV** has been proposed. Oxidative addition can then take place to give the metallocycle **LV**, which can then afford the diene via **LVI** (Noyori et al., 1975). A metallocyclic intermediate

was also proposed (Cassar and Halpern, 1970) and later confirmed as structure **LVII** (Gassman and Nikora, 1975), in the rhodium(I)-promoted reaction. Reaction of a 1,3-bishomocubane with $[Rh(CO)_2Cl]_2$ gave a complex analogous to **LVII** (Blum et al., 1975).

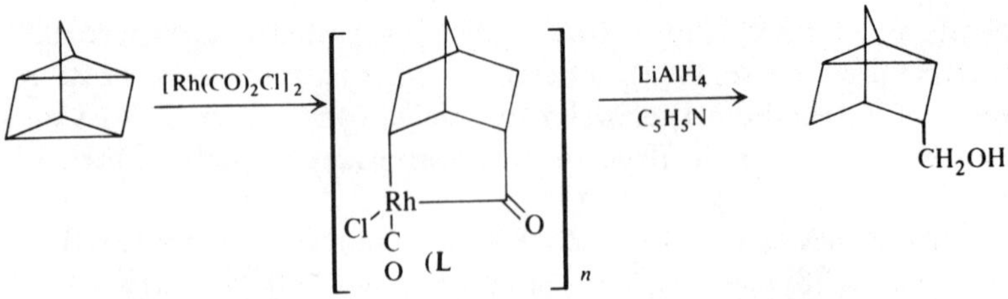

(LVII)

Hexamethyltetracyclo[2.2.0.0^{2,6}0^{3,5}] hexane (Hexamethylprismane) **(LVIII)** rearranges to hexamethyldewarbenzene **(LIX)** and hexamethylbenzene **(LX)**. Under thermal conditions, the predominant product is the

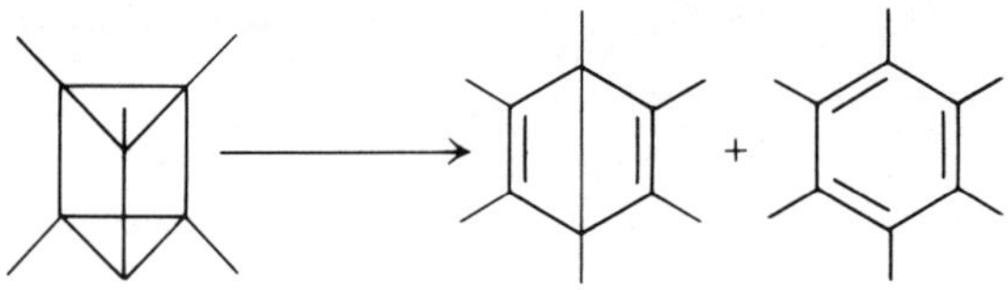

(LVIII)   **(LIX)**   **(LX)**

Heat (90°–120°)   1:30

BF$_3$–HF   1:1

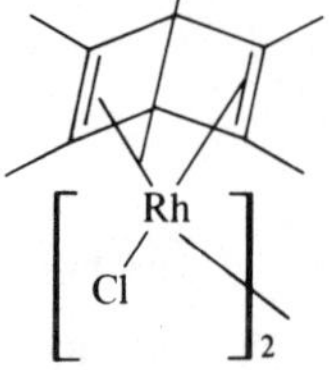

                                20:1

(LXI)

arene **LX**, while equal amounts of the two products are formed when **LVIII** is cleaved in the presence of acid. The major product is **LIX** when the easily prepared (Volger and Gaasbeek, 1968) Rh(I) complex **LXI** is used (Hogeveen and Volger, 1976b). A variety of catalysts [e.g., [Rh(CO)$_2$Cl]$_2$] catalytically decompose tri-*tert*-butylprismane (Kaiser *et al.*, 1971).

Tricyclo[3.2.2.0^{2,4}]nonatriene **(LXII)** affords bicyclo[4.2.1] nonatriene **(LXIII)** in quantitative yield as a result of reaction with chlorodicarbonylrhodium(I) dimer. By contrast, benzene and allylbenzene are formed on

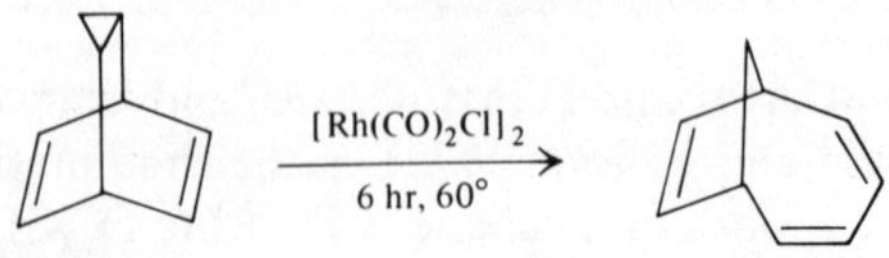

(LXII)   **(LXIII)**

pyrolysis, while irradiation of **LXII** in acetone–pentane gives barbaralone (Katz and Cerefice, 1969).

Tricyclo[2.2.0.0^{2,6}]hexane **(LXIV)** reacts with $[Rh(CO)_2Cl]_2$ to give **LXV** and **LXVI** in a 4:1 ratio (Roth and Katz, 1972). Hexamethylbenzene is

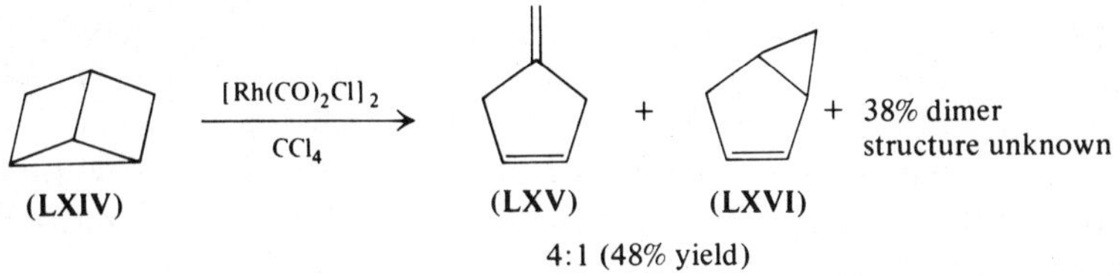

$$\xrightarrow[CCl_4]{[Rh(CO)_2Cl]_2}$$

(LXIV)   **(LXV)**   **(LXVI)**   + 38% dimer
structure unknown

4:1 (48% yield)

formed starting with the hexamethylderivative of **LXIV**, and an intermediate cyclohexadiene was isolated at $-50°$ (Hogeveen and Thio, 1973). Rhodium(I)- and iridium(I)-catalyzed rearrangements of *exo*-tricyclo-[3.2.1.0^{2,4}]oct-6-ene (Volger *et al.*, 1969a,b) and of tricyclo[3.2.1.0^{1,5}]octane (Gassman and Armour, 1971) have also been described.

B. Bicyclic Compounds

Reaction of 7-oxanorbornadienes (e.g., **LXVII**) with $[Rh(CO)_2Cl]_2$ in $CHCl_3$ affords 6-hydroxyfulvenes (e.g., **LXVIII**) in good yields (Hogeveen

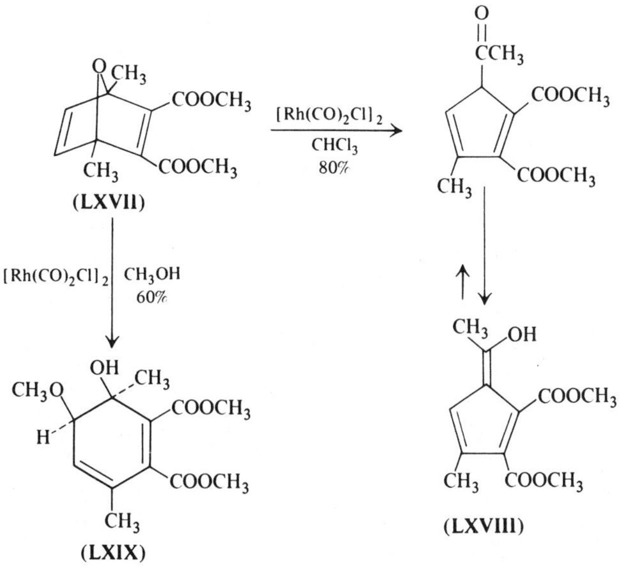

(LXVII)

$$\xrightarrow[CHCl_3]{[Rh(CO)_2Cl]_2}{80\%}$$

$[Rh(CO)_2Cl]_2$ | CH_3OH
60%

(LXIX)

(LXVIII)

and Middelkoop, 1973b; Bruggink and Hogeveen, 1972). Methoxy-cyclohexadienols such as **LXIX** result when the reaction is carried out in methanol (acidic solution) (Hogeveen and Middelkoop, 1973a; Ashworth and Berchtold, 1977a).

Exposure of bicyclo[2.1.0]pentane to $[Rh(CO)_2Cl]_2$ at 65° for 48 hr affords cyclopentene in 93% yield. Thermally, a temperature of 330° is required to bring about this rearrangement (Criegee and Rimmelin, 1957). The 1-carbomethoxy derivative gives approximately equal amounts of 1- and 3-substituted cyclopentenes (Gassman *et al.*, 1972b). The rearrangement of several other bicyclo[2.1.0]pentanes has been reported, but in unspecified yields (Wiberg and Bishop, 1973).

Methylated bicyclo[1.1.0]butanes rearrange to dienes by use of a variety of organometallic complexes (Gassman *et al.*, 1972a; Gassman and Nakai,

$Ru(CO)_3Cl_2$	74%
$Ru_3(CO)_{12}$	90%
$Mn_2(CO)_{10}$	53%
$(\pi - C_3H_5PdCl)_2$	60%
$[Rh(CO)_2Cl]_2$	85%

1972b; Gassman and Williams, 1972). The reaction is sensitive to the nature of the metal, the ligand, and the solvent in the case of $[Rh(CO)_2Cl]_2$. Phenyl-substituted bicyclo[1.1.0]butanes (e.g., **LXX**) afford cyclized products, **LXXII** and **LXXIII**, in addition to the anticipated diene **LXXI**. Metal-

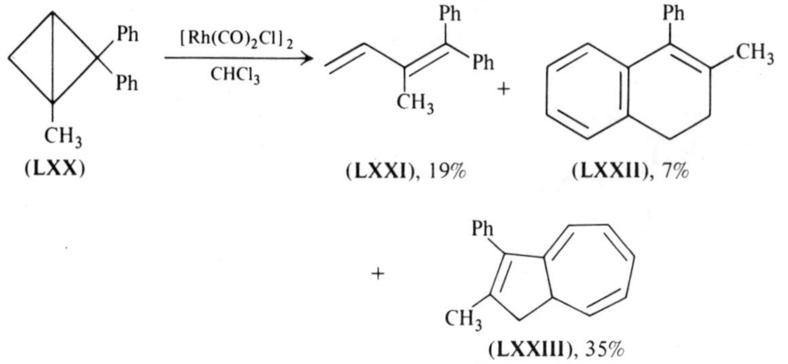

(**LXX**)

$[Rh(CO)_2Cl]_2$ / CHCl_3

(**LXXI**), 19%

+

(**LXXII**), 7%

+

(**LXXIII**), 35%

complexed carbene and metal-bonded carbonium ion intermediates have been postulated for these reactions (Gassman and Nakai, 1971, 1972a).

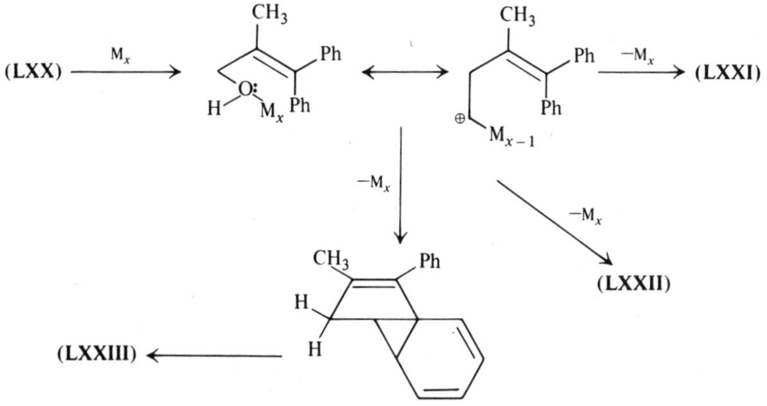

The transition metal induced rearrangement of polycyclic compounds containing the bicyclobutane ring system has been investigated by several research groups (Gassman and Atkins, 1972; Gassman and Reitz, 1973; Dauben *et al.*, 1973; Murata *et al.*, 1973; Murata and Tatsuoka, 1975). Of particular synthetic interest is the novel approach to the preparation of 1-benzothiepins by rhodium(I)-promoted rearrangement of 4,5-benzo-3-thiatricyclo[4.1.0.0^{2,7}]heptenes (**LXXIV, LXXV**) (Murata and Tatsuoka, 1975).

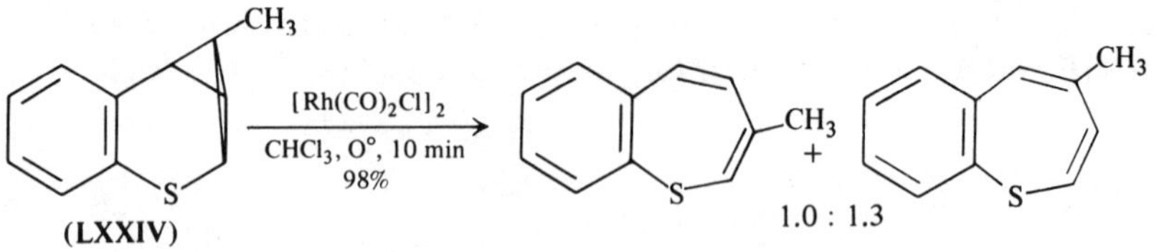

(LXXIV)

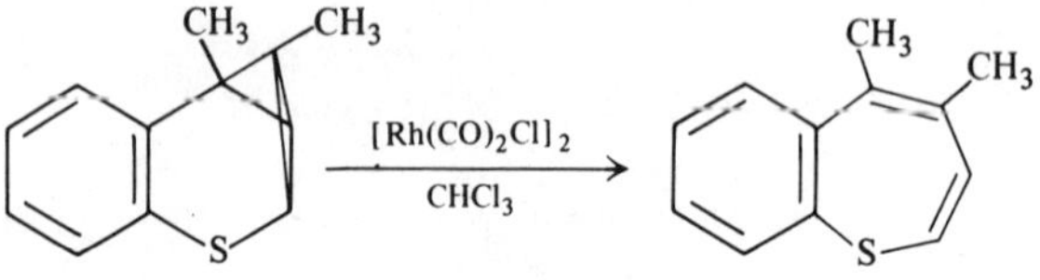

1.0 : 1.3

(LXXV)

C. Monocyclic Compounds

Rhodium(I) compounds promote the rearrangement of phenylcyclopropanes to olefins (Chum and Roth, 1975). Vinylcyclopropanes undergo interesting rearrangement and epimerization reactions in the presence of catalytic amounts of $[Rh(CO)_2Cl]_2$ (Salomon *et al.*, 1977).

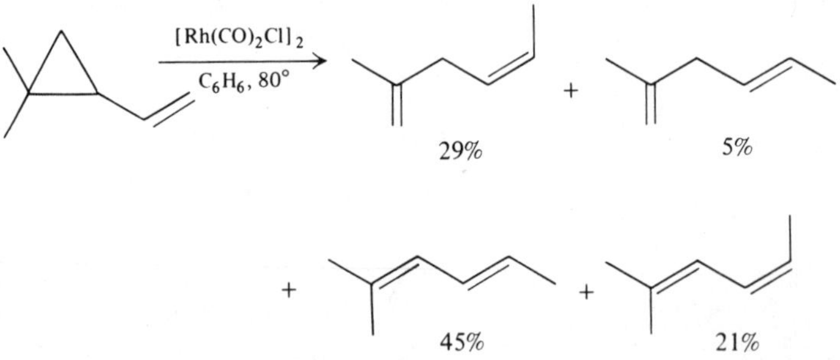

29%   5%

45%   21%

α,β-Unsaturated aldehydes are formed by the rearrangement of vinyl epoxides with $Mo(CO)_6$ (Alper *et al.*, 1976) or $[Rh(CO)_2Cl]_2$ (Adames *et al.*, 1972). The rhodium catalyst has also been used for cyclic olefinic epoxides such as norbornadiene monoepoxide (Grigg and Shelton, 1971), cyclooc-

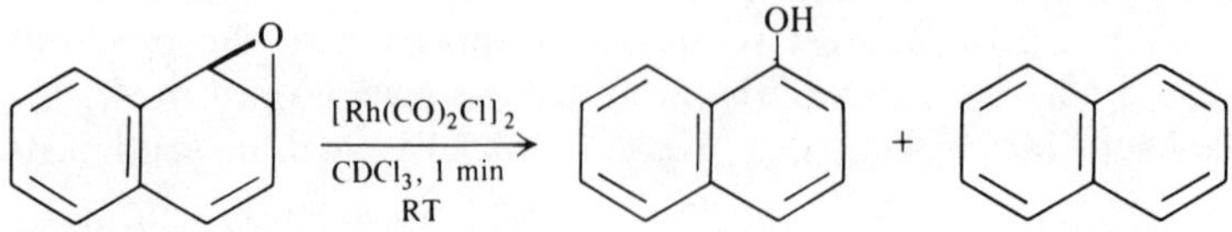

(LXXVI)

89:11

tatetraene epoxide (Grigg *et al.*, 1971), arene oxides (e.g., **LXXVI**; Ashworth and Berchtold, 1977b), and oxetanes (Adames *et al.*, 1972; Jones *et al.*, 1975). Aryl substituted epoxides can also be rearranged by $Mo(CO)_6$, ketones and olefins being formed as by-products. Carbonium ion intermediates are probably involved in these reactions (Alper *et al.*, 1976).

Ketones are the principal products formed when $(Ph_3P)_2M(CO)Cl$ [M = Rh, Ir], $(Ph_3P)_3RhCl$, $Co_2(CO)_8$, or $Co(CO)_4^-$ are employed as catalysts (Milstein *et al.*, 1974; Eisenmann, 1962).

Isoxazoles, pyrazoles, and pyrroles (**LXXVIII**) can be synthesized in high

(**LXXVII**)   (**LXXVIII**)

X = O, NAr, $CHCOOCH_3$

yields, and under remarkably mild conditions, by rearrangement of the readily available 3-phenyl-2-substituted-2*H*-azirines (**LXXVII**; X = 0, NAr, $CHCOOCH_3$) with molybdenum hexacarbonyl (Alper *et al.*, 1977b).

VII. OTHER

Treatment of aldehydes with cobalt hexaamine bis(tetracarbonyl)cobaltate gives complexes of structural type $[(RCH=NH)Co(NH_3)_5][Co(CO)_4]_2$. Exposure of the latter to bromine results in nitrile formation in variable yields (Rhee *et al.*, 1970). Hydration of nitriles to amides can be homo-

geneously catalyzed by Pt, Rh, and Ir complexes such as *trans*-Pt(CH₃)-
(NHCOCH₃)(PPh₃)₂ (Bennett and Yoshida, 1973).

REFERENCES

Abramovitch, R. A., Knaus, G. N., and Stowe, R. W. (1974). *J. Org. Chem.* **39**, 2513.
Adames, G., Bibby, C., and Grigg, R. (1972). *J. Chem. Soc., Chem. Commun.* p. 491.
Akcrmark, B., and Zetterberg, K. (1975). *Tetrahedron Lett.* p. 3733.
Albelo, G., Wiger, G., and Rettig, M. F. (1975). *J. Am. Chem. Soc.* **97**, 4510.
Alper, H. (1969a). *Angew. Chem., Int. Ed. Engl.* **8**, 677.
Alper, H. (1969b). *Tetrahedron Lett.* p. 1239.
Alper, H. (1971). *Organomet. Chem. Synth.* **1**, 69.
Alper, H. (1972a). *J. Org. Chem.* **37**, 3972.
Alper, H. (1972b). *Inorg. Chem.* **11**, 976.
Alper, H. (1973a). *J. Organomet. Chem.* **50**, 209.
Alper, H. (1973b). *J. Org. Chem.* **38**, 1417.
Alper, H. (1974). *J. Organomet. Chem.* **73**, 359.
Alper, H. (1975a). *Tetrahedron Lett.* p. 2257.
Alper, H. (1975b). *J. Organomet. Chem.* **84**, 347.
Alper, H. (1975c). *J. Org. Chem.* **40**, 2694.
Alper, H., and Edward, J. T. (1967). *J. Org. Chem.* **32**, 2938.
Alper, H., and Edward, J. T. (1968). *Can. J. Chem.* **46**, 3112.
Alper, H., and Edward, J. T. (1969). *J. Organomet. Chem.* **16**, 342.
Alper, H., and Edward, J. T. (1970). *Can. J. Chem.* **48**, 1543.
Alper, H., and Huang, C. C. (1973). *J. Org. Chem.* **38**, 64.
Alper, H., and Keung, E. C. H. (1970). *Tetrahedron Lett.* p. 53.
Alper, H., and Keung, E. C. H. (1972). *J. Org. Chem.* **37**, 2566.
Alper, H., and Paik, H. N. (1977). *J. Org. Chem.* **42**, 3522.
Alper, H., and Paik, H. N. (1978). *J. Organomet. Chem.* **144**, C18.
Alper, H., and Partis, R. A. (1972). *J. Organomet. Chem.* **35**, C40.
Alper, H., and Wall, G. (1976). *J. Chem. Soc., Chem. Commun.* p. 263.
Alper, H., Des Roches, D., Durst, T., and Legault, R. (1976). *J. Org. Chem.* **41**, 3611.
Alper, H., Des Roches, D., and des Abbayes, H. (1977a). *Angew. Chem., Int. Ed. Engl.* **16**, 41.
Alper, H., Prickett, J. E., and Wollowitz, S. (1977b). *J. Am. Chem. Soc.* **99**, 4330.
Ashby, E. C., Lin, J. J., and Kovar, R. (1976). *J. Org. Chem.* **41**, 1939.
Ashworth, R. W., and Berchtold, G. A. (1977a). *Tetrahedron Lett.* p. 339.
Ashworth, R. W., and Berchtold, G. A. (1977b). *Tetrahedron Lett.* p. 343.
Bagga, M. M., Flannigan, W. T., Knox, G. R., and Pauson, P. L. (1969). *J. Chem. Soc. C* p. 1534.
Baker, T. N., III, Mains, G. J., Sheng, M. N., and Zajacek, J. G. (1973). *J. Org. Chem.* **38**, 1145.
Bartlett, P. A., Green, F. R., III, and Webb, T. R. (1977). *Tetrahedron Lett.* p. 331.
Beck, W., Danzer, W., and Hofer, R. (1973). *Angew. Chem., Int. Ed. Engl.* **12**, 77.
Bennett, M. A., and Yoshida, T. (1973). *J. Am. Chem. Soc.* **95**, 3030.
Bertelo, C. A., and Schwartz, J. (1975). *J. Am. Chem. Soc.* **97**, 228.
Bertelo, C. A., and Schwartz, J. (1976). *J. Am. Chem. Soc.* **98**, 262.
Bird, C. W., and Hudec, J. (1959). *Chem. Ind. (London)* p. 570.
Bishop, K. C., III. (1976). *Chem. Rev.* **76**, 461.
Blackburn, T. F., Labinger, J. A., and Schwartz, J. (1975). *Tetrahedron Lett.* p. 3041.

Blum, J., and Scharf, G. (1970). *J. Org. Chem.* **35**, 1895.
Blum, J., Oppenheimer, E., and Bergmann, E. D. (1967). *J. Am. Chem. Soc.* **89**, 2338.
Blum, J., Kraus, S., and Pickholtz, Y. (1971). *J. Organomet. Chem.* **33**, 227.
Blum, J., Zlotogorski, C., and Zoran, H. (1975). *Tetrahedron Lett.* p. 1117.
Boldrini, G. P., Panunzio, M., and Umani-Ronchi, A. (1974a). *Synthesis* p. 733.
Boldrini, G. P., Panunzio, M., and Umani-Ronchi, A. (1974b). *J. Chem. Soc., Chem. Commun.* p. 359.
Boldrini, G. P., Umani-Ronchi, A., and Panunzio, M. (1976). *Synthesis* p. 596.
Booth, B. L., and Shaw, B. L. (1972). *J. Organomet. Chem.* **43**, 369.
Breslow, R., and Maresca, L. M. (1977). *Tetrahedron Lett.* p. 623.
Bruggink, A., and Hogeveen, H. (1972). *Tetrahedron Lett.* p. 4961.
Bull, J. R., and Lachmann, H. H. (1973). *Tetrahedron Lett.* p. 3055.
Bull, J. R., and Tuinman, A. (1973). *Tetrahedron Lett.* p. 4349.
Cainelli, G. F., Panunzio, M., and Umani-Ronchi, A. (1973). *Tetrahedron Lett.* p. 2491.
Cainelli, G. F., Panunzio, M., and Umani-Ronchi, A. (1975). *J. Chem. Soc., Perkin Trans. 1* p. 1273.
Cassar, L., and Halpern, J. (1970). *Chem. Commun.* p. 1082.
Cassar, L., Eaton, P. E., and Halpern, J. (1970a). *J. Am. Chem. Soc.* **92**, 3515.
Cassar, L., Eaton, P. E., and Halpern, J. (1970b). *J. Am. Chem. Soc.* **92**, 6366.
Chong, A. O., and Sharpless, K. B. (1977). *J. Org. Chem.* **42**, 1587.
Chum, P. W., and Roth, J. A. (1975). *J. Catal.* **39**, 198.
Cole, T. E., and Pettit, R. (1977). *Tetrahedron Lett.* p. 781.
Collman, J. P., Finke, R. G., Matlock, P. L., Wahren, R., Komoto, R. G., and Brauman, J. I. (1978). *J. Am. Chem. Soc.* **100**, 1119.
Colomer, E., and Corriu, R. (1975). *J. Organomet. Chem.* **82**, 367.
Corey, E. J., and Suggs, J. W. (1973). *J. Org. Chem.* **38**, 3223.
Criegee, R., and Rimmelin, A. (1957). *Chem. Ber.* **90**, 414.
Daub, J., Trautz, V., and Erhardt, U. (1972). *Tetrahedron Lett.* p. 4435.
Daub, J., Erhardt, U., Kappler, J., and Trautz, V. (1974). *J. Organomet. Chem.* **69**, 423.
Dauben, W. G., and Kielbania, A. J., Jr. (1971). *J. Am. Chem. Soc.* **93**, 7345.
Dauben, W. G., Kielbania, A. J., Jr., and Raymond, K. N. (1973). *J. Am. Chem. Soc.* **95**, 7166.
Davison, A., Krusell, W. C., and Michaelson, R. C. (1974). *J. Organomet. Chem.* **72**, C7.
de Meijere, A. (1974). *Tetrahedron Lett.* p. 1845.
de Meijere, A., and Meyer, L. U. (1974). *Tetrahedron Lett.* p. 1849.
des Abbayes, H., and Alper, H. (1977). *J. Am. Chem. Soc.* **99**, 98.
Descotes, G., and Legrand, P. (1972). *Bull. Soc. Chim. Fr.* p. 2942.
Dondoni, G., and Barbaro, G. (1975). *J. Chem. Soc., Chem. Commun.* p. 761.
Dowd, P., and Kang, K. (1974). *J. Chem. Soc., Chem. Commun.* p. 384.
Drapier, J., Hubert, A. J., and Teyssie, P. (1972). *J. Chem. Soc., Chem. Commun.* p. 484.
Drapier, J., Hubert, A. J., and Teyssie, P. (1973). *Tetrahedron Lett.* p. 419.
Drapier, J., Hubert, A. J., and Teyssie, P. (1975). *Synthesis* p. 649.
Dudley, C. W., Read, G., and Walker, P. J. C. (1974). *J. Chem. Soc., Dalton Trans.* p. 1926.
Eekhof, J. H., Hogeveen, H., and Kellogg, R. M. (1976). *J. Chem. Soc., Chem. Commun.* p. 657.
Elzinga, J., and Hogeveen, H. (1977). *J. Chem. Soc., Chem. Commun.* 705.
Eisenmann, J. (1962). *J. Org. Chem.* **27**, 2706.
Feder, H. M., and Halpern, J. (1975). *J. Am. Chem. Soc.* **97**, 7186.
Friedlina, R. Kh., and Chukovskaya, E. C. (1974). *Synthesis* p. 477.
Friedlina, R. Kh., and Velichko, F. K. (1977). *Synthesis* p. 145.
Friedman, S., Metlin, S., Svedi, A., and Wender, I. (1959). *J. Org. Chem.* **24**, 1287.

Gassman, P. G., and Armour, E. A. (1971). *Tetrahedron Lett.* p. 1431.

Gassman, P. G., and Atkins, T. J. (1972). *J. Am. Chem. Soc.* **94**, 7748.

Gassman, P. G., and Nakai, T. (1971). *J. Am. Chem. Soc.* **93**, 5897.

Gassman, P. G., and Nakai, T. (1972a). *J. Am. Chem. Soc.* **94**, 2877.

Gassman, P. G., and Nakai, T. (1972b). *J. Am. Chem. Soc.* **94**, 5497.

Gassman, P. G., and Nikora, J. A. (1975). *J. Organomet. Chem.* **92**, 81.

Gassman, P. G., and Reitz, R. R. (1973). *J. Am. Chem. Soc.* **95**, 3057.

Gassman, P. G., and Williams, F. J. (1972). *J. Am. Chem. Soc.* **94**, 7733.

Gassman, P. G., Meyer, G. R., and Williams, F. J. (1972a). *J. Am. Chem. Soc.* **94**, 7741.

Gassman, P. G., Atkins, T. J., and Lumb, J. T. (1972b). *J. Am. Chem. Soc.* **94**, 7757.

Genco, N. A., Partis, R. A., and Alper, H. (1973). *J. Org. Chem.* **38**, 4365.

Giering, W. P., Rosenblum, M., and Tancrede, J. (1972). *J. Am. Chem. Soc.* **94**, 7170.

Grigg, R., and Shelton, G. (1971). *J. Chem. Soc., Chem. Commun.* p. 1247.

Grigg, R., Hayes, R., and Sweeney, A. (1971). *J. Chem. Soc., Chem. Commun.* p. 1248.

Harrison, I. T., Kimura, E., Bohme, E., and Fried, J. H. (1969). *Tetrahedron Lett.* p. 1589.

Harrod, J. F., Knight, A. R., and McIntyre, J. S. (1972). U.S. Patent 3,654,317; (1972). *Chem. Abstr.* **76**, 140478f.

Hart, D. W., and Schwartz, J. (1974). *J. Am. Chem. Soc.* **96**, 8115.

Hart, D. W., Blackburn, T. F., and Schwartz, J. (1975). *J. Am. Chem. Soc.* **97**, 679.

Hieber, W., and Lipp, A. (1959). *Chem. Ber.* **92**, 2085.

Hirsekorn, F. J., Rakowski, M. C., and Muetterties, E. L. (1975). *J. Am. Chem. Soc.* **97**, 237.

Hoffman, R. V. (1974). *Tetrahedron Lett.* p. 2415.

Hogeveen, H., and Middelkoop, T. B. (1973a). *Tetrahedron Lett.* p. 3671.

Hogeveen, H., and Middelkoop, T. B. (1973b). *Tetrahedron Lett.* p. 4325.

Hogeveen, H., and Nusse, B. J. (1973). *Tetrahedron Lett.* p. 3667.

Hogeveen, H., and Nusse, B. J. (1974). *Tetrahedron Lett.* p. 159.

Hogeveen, H., and Thio, J. (1973). *Tetrahedron Lett.* p. 3463.

Hogeveen, H., and Volger, H. C. (1967a). *J. Am. Chem. Soc.* **89**, 2486.

Hogeveen, H., and Volger, H. C. (1967b). *Chem. Commun.* p. 1133.

Hong, P., Sonogashira, K., and Hagihara, N. (1968). *Nippon Kagaku Zasshi* **89**, 74.

Howe, G. R., and Hiatt, R. R. (1970). *J. Org. Chem.* **35**, 4007.

Howsam, R. W., and McQuillin, F. J. (1968). *Tetrahedron Lett.* p. 3667.

Iqbal, A. F. M. (1972a). *J. Org. Chem.* **37**, 2791.

Iqbal, A. F. M. (1972b). *Helv. Chim. Acta* **55**, 797.

Iqbal, A. F. M. (1975). *Tetrahedron Lett.* p. 3385.

Johnson, C. R., Herr, R. W., and Wieland, D. M. (1973). *J. Org. Chem.* **38**, 4263.

Johnson, N. A., and Gould, E. S. (1974). *J. Org. Chem.* **39**, 407.

Jones, D. N., and Knox, S. D. (1975a). *J. Chem. Soc., Chem. Commun.* p. 165.

Jones, D. N., and Knox, S. D. (1975b). *J. Chem. Soc., Chem. Commun.* p. 166.

Jones, G., II, Acquadro, M. A., and Carmody, M. A. (1975). *J. Chem. Soc., Chem. Commun.* p. 206.

Kagan, H. B. (1975). *Pure Appl. Chem.* **43**, 401.

Kaiser, K. L., Childs, R. F., and Maitlis, P. M. (1971). *J. Am. Chem. Soc.* **93**, 1270.

Katsnel'son, M. G., Kuz'mina, G. V., and Leenson, E. I. (1973). U.S.S.R. Patent 376,351; (1973). *Chem. Abstr.* **79**, 52796q.

Katz, T. J., and Cerefice, S. (1969). *Tetrahedron Lett.* p. 2561.

King, R. B., and Harmon, C. A. (1975). *J. Organomet. Chem.* **86**, 139.

Kitamura, T., Sakamoto, N., and Joh, T. (1973). *Chem. Lett.* p. 379.

Kitamura, T., Joh, T., and Hagihara, N. (1975). *Chem. Lett.* p. 203.

Kmiecik, J. E. (1965). *J. Org. Chem.* **30**, 2014.
Knifton, J. (1975). *J. Org. Chem.* **40**, 519.
Knifton, J. (1976). *J. Org. Chem.* **41**, 1200.
Kunieda, T., Tamura, T., and Takizawa, T. (1972). *J. Chem. Soc., Chem. Commun.* p. 885.
Labinger, J. A., Hart, D. W., Siebert, W. E., III, and Schwartz, J. (1975). *J. Am. Chem. Soc.* **97**, 3851.
Landesberg, J., Katz, L., and Olsen, C. (1972). *J. Org. Chem.* **37**, 930.
L'Eplattenier, F., Matthys, F., and Calderazzo, F. (1970). *Inorg. Chem.* **9**, 342.
Lindner, E., and Vitzthum, G. (1969). *Angew. Chem., Int. Ed. Engl.* **8**, 518.
Lyons, J. E. (1974). *Tetrahedron Lett.* p. 2737.
Lyons, J. E., and Turner, J. O. (1972a). *Tetrahedron Lett.* p. 2903.
Lyons, J. E., and Turner, J. O. (1972b). *J. Org. Chem.* **27**, 2881.
Magoon, E. F., Volger, H. C., Spooncer, W. W., Van Winkle, J. L., and Slaugh, L. H. (1975). *J. Organomet. Chem.* **99**, 135.
Marko, L., and Bakos, J. (1974). *J. Organomet. Chem.* **81**, 411.
Masamune, S., Bates, G. S., and Georghiou, P. E. (1974). *J. Am. Chem. Soc.* **96**, 3686.
Matlin, S., and Sammes, P. G. (1973). *J. Chem. Soc., Perkin Trans. 1* p. 2851.
Mercer, G. D., Shu, J. S., Rauchfuss, T. B., and Roundhill, D. M. (1975). *J. Am. Chem. Soc.* **97**, 1967.
Mercer, G. D., Beaulieu, W. B., and Roundhill, D. M. (1977). *J. Am. Chem. Soc.* **99**, 6551.
Merijanian, A., Mayer, T., Helling, J. F., and Klemick, F. (1972). *J. Org. Chem.* **37**, 3945.
Milstein, D., Buchman, O., and Blum, J. (1974). *Tetrahedron Lett.* p. 2257.
Mitsudo, T., Watanabe, Y., Tanaka, M., Atsuta, S., Yamamoto, K., and Takegami, Y. (1975). *Bull. Chem. Soc. Jpn.* **48**, 1506.
Mohan, A. G. (1974). U.S. Pat. 3,833,606; 1975, *Chem. Abstr.* **82**, 43410u.
Mori, Y., and Tsuji, J. (1972). *Tetrahedron* **28**, 29.
Muetterties, E. L., and Hirsekorn, F. J. (1974). *J. Am. Chem. Soc.* **96**, 4063.
Muetterties, E. L., Rakowski, M. C., Hirsekorn, F. J., Larson, W. D., Basus, V. J., and Anet, F. A. L. (1975). *J. Am. Chem. Soc.* **97**, 1266.
Murata, I., and Tatsuoka, T. (1975). *Tetrahedron Lett.* p. 2697.
Murata, I., Nakasuji, K., and Kume, H. (1973). *Tetrahedron Lett.* p. 3401.
Nelson, T. R., and Tufariello, J. J. (1975). *J. Org. Chem.* **40**, 3159.
Nesmeyanov, A. N., Friedlina, R. Kh., Chukovskaya, E. C., Petrova, K. G., and Belyavsky, A. (1962). *Tetrahedron* **17**, 61.
Normant, J. F., Cahiez, G., Chuit, C., and Villieras, J. (1974). *J. Organomet. Chem.* **77**, 269.
Noyori, R., Umeda, I., and Ishigami, T. (1972). *J. Org. Chem.* **37**, 1542.
Noyori, R., Umeda, I., Kawacichi, H., and Takaya, H. (1975). *J. Am. Chem. Soc.* **97**, 812.
Ohno, K., and Tsuji, J. (1968). *J. Am. Chem. Soc.* **90**, 99.
Onoda, T., and Masai, H. (1974). Japan Kokai 74/126,633.
Paquette, L. A., Boggs, R. A., Farnham, W. B., and Beckley, R. S. (1975a). *J. Am. Chem. Soc.* **97**, 1112.
Paquette, L. A., Boggs, R. A., and Ward, J. S. (1975b). *J. Am. Chem. Soc.* **97**, 1118.
Posner, G. H., and Ting, J. S. (1973). *Synth. Commun.* **3**, 281.
Rakowski, M. C., Hirsekorn, F. J., Stuhl, L. S., and Muetterties, E. L. (1976). *Inorg. Chem.* **15**, 2379.
Rhee, I., Ryang, M., and Tsutsumi, S. (1970). *Tetrahedron Lett.* p. 3419.
Rosenblum, M., Saidi, M. R., and Madhavarao, M. (1975). *Tetrahedron Lett.* p. 4009.
Roth, R. J., and Katz, T. J. (1972). *J. Am. Chem. Soc.* **94**, 4770.
Russell, M. J., White, C., and Maitlis, P. M. (1977). *J. Chem. Soc., Chem. Commun.* p. 427.

Saegusa, T., Ito, T., and Shimizu, T. (1970). *J. Org. Chem.* **35**, 3995.
Salomon, R. G., Salomon, M. F., and Kachinski, J. L. C. (1977). *J. Am. Chem. Soc.* **99**, 1043.
Scott, L. T., and Cotton, W. D. (1973). *J. Chem. Soc., Chem. Commun.* p. 320.
Semmelhack, M. F., and Stauffer, R. D. (1973). *Tetrahedron Lett.* p. 2667.
Sharpless, K. B., and Michaelson, R. C. (1973). *J. Am. Chem. Soc.* **95**, 6136.
Sharpless, K. B., Akashi, K. A., and Oshima, K. (1976). *Tetrahedron Lett.* p. 2503.
Sheldon, R. A. (1973a). *Recl. Trav. Chim. Pays-Bas* **92**, 253.
Sheldon, R. A. (1973b). *Recl. Trav. Chim. Pays-Bas* **92**, 367.
Sheldon, R. A., and Kochi, J. K. (1976). *Adv. Catal.* **25**, 272.
Sheldon, R. A., and Van Doorn, J. A. (1973). *J. Catal.* **31**, 427.
Sheldon, R. A., Van Doorn, J. A., Schram, C. W. A., and De Jong, A. J. (1973). *J. Catal.* **31**, 438.
Sheng, M. N. (1972). *Synthesis* p. 194.
Sheng, M. N., and Zajacek, J. G. (1968a). *Adv. Chem. Ser.* **76**, 418.
Sheng, M. N., and Zajacek, J. G. (1968b). *J. Org. Chem.* **33**, 588.
Sheng, M. N., and Zajacek, J. G. (1970). *J. Org. Chem.* **35**, 1839.
Smetana, R. D. (1972). U.S. Patent 3,657,251; (1972). *Chem. Abstr.* **77**, 5355u.
Spadlo, M. (1974). *Przem. Chem.* **53**, 84.
Strohmeier, W., and Pfohler, P. (1976). *J. Organomet. Chem.* **108**, 393.
Suggs, J. W. (1978). *J. Am. Chem. Soc.* **100**, 640.
Takaya, H., Yamakawa, M., and Noyori, R. (1973). *Chem. Lett.* p. 781.
Tamura, T., Kunieda, T., and Takizawa, T. (1972). *Tetrahedron Lett.* p. 2219.
Tanaka, S., Yamamoto, H., Nozaki, H., Sharpless, K. B., Michaelson, R. C., and Cutting, J. D. (1974). *J. Am. Chem. Soc.* **96**, 5254.
Tolstikov, G. A., Dzhemilev, U. M., and Yur'ev, V. P. (1971a). *J. Org. Chem. USSR (Engl. Transl.)* **8**, 1200.
Tolstikov, G. A., Dzhemilev, U. M., and Yur'ev, V. P. (1971b). *J. Org. Chem. USSR (Engl. Transl.)* **8**, 1204.
Tolstikov, G. A., Jenilev, U. M., Jurjev, V. P., Gershanov, F. B., and Rafikov, S. R. (1971c). *Tetrahedron Lett.* p. 2807.
Tolstikov, G. A., Dzhemilev, U. M., Novitskaya, N. N., and Yur'ev, V. P. (1972). *Bull. Acad. Sci. USSR, Div. Chem. Sci.* **21**, 2675.
Tolstikov, G. A., Yur'ev, V. P., and Gailyunas, I. A. (1973). *Bull. Acad. Sci. USSR, Div. Chem. Sci.* **22**, 1395.
Tolstikov, G. A., Yur'ev, V. P., and Dzhemilov, U. M. (1975). *Russ. Chem. Rev.* **44**, 319.
Trost, B. M., and Chen, F. (1971). *Tetrahedron Lett.* p. 2603.
Trost, B. M., and Ziman, S. D. (1973). *J. Org. Chem.* **38**, 932.
Tsuji, J., and Ohno, K. (1969). *Synthesis* p. 157.
Tyrlik, S., and Wolochowicz, I. (1975). *J. Chem. Soc., Chem. Commun.* p. 781.
Vedejs, E., Salomon, M. F., and Weeks, P. D. (1972). *J. Organomet. Chem.* **40**, 221.
Velichko, F. K., and Vinogradova, L. V. (1975). *Izv. Akad. Nauk SSSR, Ser. Khim.* p. 1575.
Villieras, J., Disnar, J. R., Masure, D., and Normant, J. F. (1973). *J. Organomet. Chem.* **57**, C95.
Volger, H. C., and Gaasbeek, M. M. P. (1968). *Recl. Trav. Chim. Pays-Bas* **87**, 1290.
Volger, H. C., Hogeveen, H., and Gaasbeek, M. M. P. (1969a). *J. Am. Chem. Soc.* **91**, 218.
Volger, H. C., Hogeveen, H., and Gaasbeek, M. M. P. (1969b). *J. Am. Chem. Soc.* **91**, 2137.
Wada, F., and Matsuda, T. (1973). *Nippon Kagaku Kaishi*, 2177.
Walborsky, H. M., and Allen, L. E. (1971). *J. Am. Chem. Soc.* **93**, 5465.
Watanabe, Y., Yamashita, M., Mitsudo, T., Tanaka, M., and Takegami, Y. (1973). *Tetrahedron Lett.* p. 3535.
Watanabe, Y., Yamashita, M., Mitsudo, T., Tanaka, M., and Takegami, Y. (1974a). *Tetrahedron*

Lett. p. 1879.

Watanabe, Y., Mitsudo, T., Yamashita, M., Shim, S. C., and Takegami, Y. (1974b). *Chem. Lett.* p. 1265.

Watanabe, Y., Yamashita, M., Mitsudo, T., Igami, M., Tonsi, K., and Takegami, Y. (1975). *Tetrahedron Lett.* p. 1063.

Watanabe, Y., Shim, S. C., Mitsudo, T., Yamashita, M., and Takegami, Y. (1976a). *Bull. Chem. Soc. Jpn.* **49**, 2302.

Watanabe, Y., Yamashita, M., Igami, M., Mitsudo, T., and Takegami, Y. (1976b). *Bull. Chem. Soc. Jpn.* **49**, 2824.

Wender, I., Levine, R., and Orchin, M. (1950). *J. Am. Chem. Soc.* **72**, 4375.

Wender, I., Greenfield, H., and Orchin, M. (1951). *J. Am. Chem. Soc.* **73**, 2656.

Wiberg, K. B., and Bishop, K. C., III. (1973). *Tetrahedron Lett.* p. 2727.

Yamashita, M., Watanabe, Y., Mitsudo, T., and Takegami, Y. (1975). *Tetrahedron Lett.* p. 1867.

Yamashita, M., Watanabe, Y., Mitsudo, T., and Takegami, Y. (1976). *Bull. Chem. Soc. Jpn.* **49**, 3597.

Yur'ev, V. P., Gailyunas, I. A., Isaeva, Z. G., and Tolstikov, G. A. (1974). *Bull. Acad. Sci. USSR, Div. Chem. Sci.* **23**, 885.

Yur'ev, V. P., Gailyunas, I. A., Spirikhin, L. V., and Tolstikov, G. A. (1975). *J. Gen. Chem. USSR (Engl. Transl.)* **45**, 2269.

AUTHOR INDEX

Numbers in italics refer to the pages on which the complete references are listed.

G

H

172 AUTHOR INDEX

Nikora, J. A., 151, *160*
Nivert, C. L., 48, 49, 50, *62*
Normant, J. F., 131, 143, *161, 162*
Norton, J. R., 45, *59*
Novitskaya, N. N., 128, *162*
Noyori, R., 134, 144, 150, 151, *161, 162*
Nozaki, H., 123, *162*
Nusse, B. J., 151, *160*
Nyathi, J. Z., 44, *59*
Nyholm, R. S., 10, *59*
Nystrom, R. F., 76, *119*

O

O'Connor, J. P., 55, *62*
Odenigbo, G., 30, 32, 37, *61*
Ofele, K., 68, *117, 119*
Ohno, K., 147, *161, 162*
Olsen, C., 137, *161*
Onoda, T., 139, *161*
Oppenheimer, E., 147, *159*
Orchin, M., 129, *163*
Oshima, K., 127, *162*
Otsuka, S., 2, 3, 4, 26, 27, 32, 34, *61*
Owston, P. G., 4, *59*

P

Paik, H. N., 139, 148, *158*
Pályi, G., 41, 46, 56, *61, 62*
Pannekoek, W. J., 84, *119*
Panunzio, M., 134, 144, *159*
Paquette, L. A., 150, *161*
Parshall, G. W., 7, *59*, 98, *119*
Partis, R. A., 136, 139, *158, 160*
Pasynskii, A. A., 6, *61*
Patel, C. G., 4, *59*
Patin, H., 66, *117*
Pauson, P. L., 38, 39, 41, 53, 54, *58, 59, 60, 61, 62*, 66, 86, 98, 99, *115, 117, 118, 119*, 138, *158*
Penfold, B. R., 46, *62*
Peterlik, M., 76, *119*
Petrova, K. G., 143, *161*
Petrovskii, P. V., 71, *118*

Pettit, R., 12, 14, *61*, 69, 70, 71, *116, 117*, 131, *159*
Pfeffer, M., 98, *116*
Pfohler, P., 147, *162*
Piacenti, F., 46, *61*
Pickholtz, Y., 147, *159*
Pittman, C. U., Jr., 55, *62*, 108, *119*
Pollock, D. F., 30, *62*
Posner, G. H., 146, *161*
Preston, F. J., 98, *115*
Pribytkova, I. M., 45, *63*
Price, J. T., 69, *119*
Prickett, J. E., 157, *158*
Puddephatt, R. J., 27, *59*

R

Rafikov, S. R., 127, 128, *162*
Raju, J. R., 76, 79, *116*
Rakowski, M. C., 129, *160, 161*
Randell, E. W., 69, 76, *116*
Rauchfuss, T. B., 127, *161*
Rausch, M. D., 81, *119*
Rawlinson, R. M., 69, *116*
Raymond, K. N., 155, *159*
Read, G., 126, *159*
Reed, H. W. B., 46, *59*
Reed, R. I., 98, *115*
Rees, C. W., 9, *60*
Reeves, P. C., 69, *120*
Reitz, R. R., 155, *160*
Rejoan, A., 107, 108, *116*
Reppe, W., 30, *62*
Rettig, M. F., 130, *158*
Rhee, I., 157, *161*
Ridaura, V. E., 68, *115, 118*
Rimmelin, A., 154, *159*
Ritchey, W. M., 6, *63*
Rivera, J., 10, *61*
Roberts, G. C., 107, 110, *117*
Robertson, G. B., 7, 8, *58, 62*
Robinson, B. H., 46, 48, 57, 58, *60, 62*
Robinson, G., 35, 41, *61*
Roe, D. M., 9, *62*
Rogerson, T. D., 82, *119*
Root, W. G., 101, 102, 103, 104, *115*
Rosenblum, M., 132, 133, *160, 161*

Vizi-Orosz, A., 41, *62*
Vohwinkel, F., 111, *118, 120*
Volger, H. C., 142, 151, 152, 153, *160, 161,*
    162
Vol'kenau, N. A., 84, *118*
Vollhardt, K. P. C., 37, 43, *60, 63*
Vol'pin, M. E., 107, 114, *120*
von Hobe, D., 6, *62*
von Werner, K., 27, *59*
Voyevodskaya, T. I., 45, *63*

W

Wada, F., 134, *162*
Wahren, R., 134, *159*
Wakamatsu, H., 41, 46, 53, 57, *60, 63*
Wakatsuki, T., 7, 31, 33, 34, 36, 39, 43, *63*
Wakatsuki, Y., 30, 39, 40, 44, 45, *63,* 107,
    120
Walborsky, H. M., 147, *162*
Walker, P. J. C., 80, 85, 86, *120,* 126, *159*
Wall, G., 140, *158*
Wan, K. Y., 4, *59*
Ward, J. S., 150, *161*
Watanabe, Y., 134, 135, 144, 150, *161, 162,*
    163
Watts, W. E., 38, 41, 53, 54, *60, 61, 62,* 71,
    86, *116, 118*
Webb, T. R., 127, *158*
Weeks, P. D., 126, *162*
Wehman, A. T., 11, 52, *62*
Wells, D. K., 69, *119*
Wender, I., 11, 19, 41, 46, 54, *61, 62,* 107,
    119, 129, *159, 163*
Wheatley, P. J., 66, *120*
Whimp, P. O., 7, 8, *58, 62*
White, A. M. S., 76, *116*
White, C., 129, *162*
White, D. L., 20, *62*
White, J. F., 113, 114, *120*
Whiting, M. C., 69, 71, 76, *119*
Wiberg, K. B., 154, *163*
Wieland, D. M., 133, *160*
Wiger, G., 130, *158*
Wilen, S. H., 94, *120*
Wilkinson, G., 6, 7, 9, *58, 59, 60,* 84, *118*
Wilkinson, J. R., 4, *63*
Williams, F. J., 154, *160*

Williams, G. H., 48, 49, 50, 51, 52, 53, *62*
Wilson, C. A., 100, *115*
Winkler, H. J. S., 66, *120*
Winter, W., 32, *61*
Wollowitz, S., 157, *158*
Wolochowicz, I., 132, *162*
Wong, C. S., 24, 25, *59*
Wong, K. L. T., 6, *63*
Woodward, P., 44, *59*
Woon, P. S., 112, *117, 120*
Wotiz, J. H., 11, 62, *63*
Wrighton, M. S., 109, 110, *119, 120*
Wu, A., 69, *120*
Wurbels, G. G., 83, *120*

Y

Yagupsky, G., 109, *120*
Yamagami, N., 46, 53, 57, *63*
Yamakawa, M., 150, *162*
Yamamoto, H., 123, *162*
Yamamoto, K., 135, *161*
Yamamoto, Y., 44, *63*
Yamamura, M., 98, 99, *118, 120*
Yamashita, M., 134, 144, 150, *162, 163*
Yamazaki, H., 7, 30, 31, 33, 34, 36, 39, 40,
    42, 43, 44, 45, *63*
Yamazaki, Y., 107, *120*
Yoshida, T., 158, *158*
Yoshida, Y., 8, *58*
Yoshifuji, M., 77, 81, *119*
Yuguchi, S., 110, *119*
Yur'ev, V. P., 122, 123, 127, 128, *162, 163*

Z

Zajacek, J. G., 122, 124, 127, *158, 162*
Zakharkin, L. I., 111, *120*
Zanarotti, A., 68, *115*
Zdanovitch, V. I., 69, 76, *118*
Zeiss, H., 30, *63,* 66, *120*
Zetterberg, K., 143, *158*
Ziman, S. D., 147, *162*
Zimmer, H. J., 111, *120*
Zingales, F., 29, *61*
Zlotogorski, C., 151, *159*
Zoran, H., 151, *159*

SUBJECT INDEX

A

Acetalization, 145
Acetophenone, 82
α-Acetoxy ketones, 131
Acid halides, 147
Acetylacetone, 15, 16
Acid chlorides, 131, 149
Acrylonitrile, 56, 57
Addition reactions,
  aldehydes, 144–145
  alkenes, 141–143
  alkynes, 143
  π-allyl complexes, 143
  ketones, 144
Aldehydes, 131, 144–145, 150, 157
Alkenes, 16, 17, 24, 25, 27, 48, 56, 106, 122–126, 129, 130, 132, 133, 141–143, 146–148, 154–157
Alkylation, 72–75, 93–95, 113–114
Alkylidynetricobalt nonacarbonyl complexes, 19, 45–58
  carbonium ion derivatives, 51–52
  as catalysts, 55–58
  as intermediates, 52–55
  synthesis, 19, 45–52
Alkyne–metal complexes, see Metal–alkyne complexes
Alkynes, 5, 6, 7, 9, 11–14, 16, 23–39, 43–44, 53, 56, 67, 112, 143, 147
Allyl chloride, 122
π-Allyl complexes, 126–127, 129, 143, 146, 154
Aluminum chloride, 75, 77
Amidines, 136

Amines, 86, 89, 135–139, 142, 143
Aminomethylation, 142
tert-Amyl hydroperoxide, 122–124, 127, 128
Anhydrides, 134–135, 147–148,
  thio, 147–148
Aniline, 127, 137
Anisole, 15
Anthracene, 85, 129
η^6-Arene-η^5-cyclopentadienyliron cations, 84, 85, 87, 88
Arene–metal complexes, see Metal–arene complexes
Arenes, 80, 81
Aromatization, 97–98
2H-Azirines, 157
Azobisisobutyronitrile, 48
Azo compounds, 99, 100, 106, 128, 136–139, 146
Azoxybenzenes, 128, 136–138
Azulenes, 67

B

Barbaralone, 153
Benchrotrene, see Metal–arene complexes
Benzaldehyde, 99
Benzene-d_6, 129
(Benzene)tetracobalt nonacarbonyl, 139
Benzil, 126
Benzocyclobutene, 37
Benzohydroxamoyl chlorides, 135–136
Benzoic acid, 126
(Benzoic acid)chromium tricarbonyl, 71

177

Organolithium compounds, 48, 81, 87, 99,
    130, 131, 134
Organomercury compounds, 47, 48
Organosilanes, 48, 49, 50
Organozirconium compounds, 141, 143
7-Oxanorbornadienes, 153
12-Oxa[4.4.3]propella-2,4,7,9-tetraene, 109
Oxaziridines, 127
Oxidation, 122–128 (see also
    Decomplexation)
  alcohols, 127
  alkenes, 122–126
  π-allylcomplexes, 126–127
  amines, 127
  azocompounds, 128
  diphenylacetylene, 126
  ketones, 127
  nitro compounds, 127
  organozirconium compounds, 141
  Schiff bases, 127–128
  sulfides, 128
Oxidative addition, 82
Oxides,
  nitrogen, 136
  phosphorus, 139
  sulfur, 139–140
Oximes, 135, 106
Ozonide, 127

P

Pentacarbonylchromate, 144
Pentafluorophenylmagnesium bromide, 9
Pentamethylcyclopentadienylrhodium
    dichloride dimer, 129
Pentaphenylpyrrole, 34
trans-3-Penten-2-ol, 123
Perfluorocyclohexa-1,3-diene, 9
Perfluorofluorenone, 9
Phase transfer catalysis, 137, 73, 93
Phenylacetaldehyde, 53
Phenylacetylene, 112
1,3 exo-N-Phenylbenzisoindoline, 99
2-Phenyl-2-butene, 27
4H-4-Phenylcyclopenta(c)cinnoline, 107
2-Phenylethyl chloride, 71
Phenylhydrazones, 106

2-Phenyl-2H-indazole, 138–139
Phenylmesitylene, 87
trans-1-Phenyl-1-propene, 143
2-Phenyl-1,2,3-triazole, 100
Phosphineimines, 139
Phthalazine, 135
Phthalic anhydride, 135
Polymerization, 56, 57, 110–113
Potassium borohydride, 89, 91, 92, 94–96
Propyne, 56
Protecting Groups, 149–150
Pyrazoles, 157
Pyridines, 31, 43
Pyridinium perbromide, 20
Pyrroles, 49, 157

Q

Quadricyclane, 151, 152
2-Quinolones, 107

R

Rearrangements, 150–157
Reduction, 128–140
  π-allyl complexes, 129
  σ,π-allyl complexes, 130
  anhydrides, 134–135
  arenechromium complexes, 89–92, 95, 96
  aromatic hydrocarbons, 128–129
  azo compounds, 137
  azoxy compounds, 136–137
  benzohydroxamoyl chlorides, 136
  diazines, 135
  enamines, 135
  epoxides, 132–133
  halides, 130–132
  ketones, 134
  nitro compounds, 137–139
  nitrones, 136
  nitroso compounds, 139
  nitroxyl radicals, 137
  N-oxides, 136
  oximes, 135–136
  oxygen, 114–115
  phosphine oxides, 139

ORGANIC CHEMISTRY
A SERIES OF MONOGRAPHS

EDITOR

HARRY H. WASSERMAN
Department of Chemistry
Yale University
New Haven, Connecticut

1. Wolfgang Kirmse. CARBENE CHEMISTRY, 1964; 2nd Edition, 1971

2. Brandes H. Smith. BRIDGED AROMATIC COMPOUNDS, 1964

3. Michael Hanack. CONFORMATION THEORY, 1965

4. Donald J. Cram. FUNDAMENTALS OF CARBANION CHEMISTRY, 1965

5. Kenneth B. Wiberg (Editor). OXIDATION IN ORGANIC CHEMISTRY, PART A, 1965; Walter S. Trahanovsky (Editor). OXIDATION IN ORGANIC CHEMISTRY, PART B, 1973; PART C, 1978

6. R. F. Hudson. STRUCTURE AND MECHANISM IN ORGANO-PHOSPHORUS CHEMISTRY, 1965

7. A. William Johnson. YLID CHEMISTRY, 1966

8. Jan Hamer (Editor). 1,4-CYCLOADDITION REACTIONS, 1967

9. Henri Ulrich. CYCLOADDITION REACTIONS OF HETEROCUMULENES, 1967

10. M. P. Cava and M. J. Mitchell. CYCLOBUTADIENE AND RELATED COMPOUNDS, 1967

11. Reinhard W. Hoffmann. DEHYDROBENZENE AND CYCLOALKYNES, 1967

12. Stanley R. Sandler and Wolf Karo. ORGANIC FUNCTIONAL GROUP PREPARATIONS, VOLUME I, 1968; VOLUME II, 1971; VOLUME III, 1972

13. Robert J. Cotter and Markus Matzner. RING-FORMING POLYMERIZATIONS, PART A, 1969; PART B, 1; B, 2, 1972

14. R. H. DeWolfe, CARBOXYLIC ORTHO ACID DERIVATIVES, 1970

15. R. Foster. ORGANIC CHARGE-TRANSFER COMPLEXES, 1969

16. James P. Snyder (Editor). NONBENZENOID AROMATICS, VOLUME I, 1969; VOLUME II, 1971

17. C. H. Rochester. ACIDITY FUNCTIONS, 1970

18. Richard J. Sundberg. THE CHEMISTRY OF INDOLES, 1970

19. A. R. Katritzky and J. M. Lagowski. CHEMISTRY OF THE HETEROCYCLIC N-OXIDES, 1970

20. Ivar Ugi (Editor). ISONITRILE CHEMISTRY, 1971

188   ORGANIC CHEMISTRY

21. G. Chiurdoglu (Editor). CONFOR-
MATIONAL ANALYSIS, 1971

22. Gottfried Schill. CATENANES, ROTAX-
ANES, AND KNOTS, 1971

23. M. Liler. REACTION MECHANISMS IN
SULPHURIC ACID AND OTHER STRONG
ACID SOLUTIONS, 1971

24. J. B. Stothers. CARBON-13 NMR
SPECTROSCOPY, 1972

25. Maurice Shamma. THE ISOQUINO-
LINE ALKALOIDS: CHEMISTRY AND
PHARMACOLOGY, 1972

26. Samuel P. McManus (Editor). OR-
GANIC REACTIVE INTERMEDIATES,
1973

27. H. C. Van der Plas. RING TRANSFOR-
MATIONS OF HETEROCYCLES, VOL-
UMES 1 AND 2, 1973

28. Paul N. Rylander. ORGANIC SYNTHE-
SES WITH NOBLE CATALYSTS, 1973

29. Stanley R. Sandler and Wolf Karo.
POLYMER SYNTHESES, VOLUME I,
1974; VOLUME II, 1977

30. Robert T. Blickenstaff, Anil C.
Ghosh, and Gordon C. Wolf. TOTAL
SYNTHESIS OF STEROIDS, 1974

31. Barry M. Trost and Lawrence S.
Melvin, Jr. SULFUR YLIDES: EMERG-
ING SYNTHETIC INTERMEDIATES, 1975

32. Sidney D. Ross, Manuel Finkelstein,
and Eric J. Rudd. ANODIC OXIDATION,
1975

33. Howard Alper (Editor). TRANSITION
METAL ORGANOMETALLICS IN OR-
GANIC SYNTHESIS, VOLUME I, 1976;
VOLUME II, 1978

34. R. A. Jones and G. P. Bean. THE
CHEMISTRY OF PYRROLES, 1976

35. Alan P. Marchand and Roland E.
Lehr (Editors). PERICYCLIC REAC-
TIONS, VOLUME I, 1977; VOLUME II,
1977

36. Pierre Crabbé (Editor). PROSTAGLAN-
DIN RESEARCH, 1977

37. Eric Block. REACTIONS OF ORGANO-
SULFUR COMPOUNDS, 1978

38. Arthur Greenberg and Joel F. Lieb-
man, STRAINED ORGANIC MOLECULES,
1978

39. Philip S. Bailey. OZONATION IN OR-
GANIC CHEMISTRY, VOL. I, 1978

40. Harry H. Wasserman and Robert W.
Murray (Editors). SINGLET OXYGEN,
1978